50

MATHS LESSONS FOR LESS ABLE LEARNERS

- Tricky topics covered
- Ideas to build confidence
- Photocopiable activities

AGES 9-11

Bob Ansell

Credits

Author
Bob Ansell

Editor
Sally Gray

Assistant Editors
Niamh O'Carroll & Victoria Lee

Illustrations
Garry Davies

Series Designer
Micky Pledge

Designers
Erik Ivens & Micky Pledge

Text © Bob Ansell
© 2006 Scholastic Ltd

Designed using Adobe InDesign

Published by Scholastic Ltd
Villiers House
Clarendon Avenue
Leamington Spa
Warwickshire CV32 5PR

www.scholastic.co.uk

Printed by Bell and Bain Ltd, Glasgow.

3 4 5 6 7 8 9   7 8 9 0 1 2 3 4 5

British Library Cataloguing-in-Publication Data
A catalogue record for this book is available from the British Library.

ISBN 0-439-96521-7
ISBN 978-0439-96521-7

The right of Bob Ansell to be identified as the author of this work has been asserted by him in accordance with the Copyright, Designs and Patents Act 1988.

Extracts from The National Numeracy Strategy © Crown copyright. Reproduced under the terms of HMSO Guidance Note 8.

Contents

Introduction

About the series

50 Maths Lessons for Less Able Learners is a series of three books designed for teachers and learning support assistants working with lower ability children within the daily mathematics lesson. Each book covers a two-year span of the primary age range: KS1 5-7 and KS2 7-9 and 9-11.

Each title consists of 50 oral and mental starter activities and 50 lesson plans. Each lesson plan comes with an accompanying photocopiable activity page. The activities cover many of the objectives in the National Numeracy Strategy's *Framework for Teaching Mathematics* (DfEE).

The lesson plans and accompanying photocopiable activities are designed to:
● Support less confident learners with a range of key mathematical concepts.
● Motivate children with engaging activities and games.
● Suggest ways to modify activities to address different learning styles.
● Fit into the individual teacher's existing planning for mathematics.

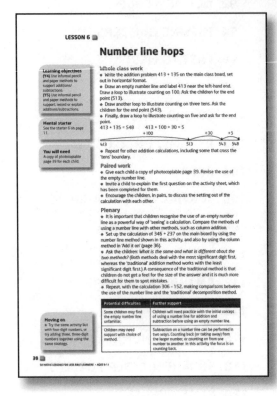

How to use this book

This book begins with a detailed 'Objectives grid', which gives an overview of the objectives addressed by each lesson. Teachers can also use this grid to track backwards to identify appropriate objectives from previous years where necessary. A bank of '50 oral and mental starters' has then been included. Links to appropriate starters are made on each lesson plan. However, they can also be used flexibly as required – for example, you might want to map similar oral and mental starters with the theme of the main teaching activities; use them to introduce later teaching; or use them to consolidate previous teaching. They might also be used as focused oral assessment activities with small groups. A set of target questions has been given for this purpose.

To make the books in this series easy to use all 50 lesson plans follow the same format.

Learning objectives

Each lesson is written to address one or more of the NNS objectives from Years 4, 5 and 6. The grid at the front of the book tracks back to show how an objective tracks back.

Mental starter

A suggested linked mental starter activity from the bank of starters at the front of the book (pages 10-27).

Whole class work

Introduces the context and concept of each lesson to the whole class.

Group work

This details the teaching activity to be undertaken by groups of less able learners, led by the class teacher or a teaching assistant. Various teaching strategies are used, and knowledge and skills are presented creatively to engage children and appeal to different learning styles. Opportunities for children to talk about their work and explain their ideas and understanding are offered throughout. The activities are designed to build on what the children already know – the aim being to build confidence. Emphasis is placed on active participation by the children through the use of games, role-play and so on. Suggested questions and opportunities for teacher intervention are also included (see below for further information).

Independent/paired work

Where appropriate, an individual or paired activity is suggested. These provide opportunities for the less confident children to work with greater independence. The activities suggested are intended to reinforce and consolidate the learning that takes place in the teacher led part of the lesson and include a variety of games, reinforcement activities or problems to solve. Many of the activities can be easily adapted to use on more than one occasion.

Plenary

Where possible the plenary offers an opportunity to reflect on the less confident children's understanding of the lesson objective.

Potential difficulties and further support

This grid outlines the potential difficulties that the children might experience. Suggestions for further differentiating the activities for children who require extra support are provided, as well as notes on adapting the activities for children's different learning styles.

Moving on

At the end of each plan, ideas are included for how to help the children who have met the objectives to progress further.

Interventions

The NNS suggests that 'as far as possible, children should work together'. This inclusive approach therefore requires a variety of intervention techniques for children working significantly below expected levels of attainment. The NNS identifies three waves of possible interventions, as outlined above. These include whole class teaching for all children (wave 1), interventions in small groups with the teacher or learning support assistants (wave 2) and targeted interventions with individuals (wave 3). The lessons in this book reflect this approach with opportunities for different types of intervention offered throughout.

The broad curriculum

The *50 Maths Lessons for Less Able Learners* series sits comfortably within the principles underpinning aspects of 'Excellence and Enjoyment' (DfES, 2004), giving renewed emphasis to matters of inclusive practice and flexible curriculum planning.

Ofsted's report for 2002 confirmed that the National Numeracy Strategy continues to have a positive impact on the teaching of pupils with special educational needs. Their report also confirms that almost all pupils with special educational needs are included in the daily mathematics lesson.

The *50 Maths Lessons* series features numerous activities that call on the child to apply knowledge and understanding to wider contexts, but within an environment tailored more to the needs of the less confident learner. Through skilful and timely intervention the child is likely to be well placed to benefit from this modified programme. At the same time, the incorporation of common themes and whole class activity minimises the possibility of the child feeling excluded or marginalised.

Title of lesson	Tracking back Year 4 objectives	Year 5 objectives	Tracking forwards Year 6 objectives
1 Word sort	● Read and write whole numbers to at least 10 000 in figures and words.	● Read and write whole numbers in figures and in words, and know what each digit represents.	
2 Star numbers	● Give one or more numbers lying between two given numbers. ● Read and write the vocabulary of comparing and ordering numbers.	Give one or more numbers lying between two given numbers.	
3 Three in a row	● Order a set of whole numbers less than 10000	● **Order a given set of positive integers.**	
4 Don't cross the line	● Read and write whole numbers to 10 000 and know what each digit represents.	● **Order a given set of positive integers**.	
5 Add it on	● Use informal pencil and paper methods to support additions.	● Use informal pencil and paper methods to support, record or explain additions and subtractions.	
6 Number line hops	● Use informal pencil and paper methods to support additions and subtractions.	● Use informal pencil and paper methods to support, record or explain additions and subtractions.	
7 At the fairground	● **Choose and use appropriate number operations and ways of calculating to solve problems,** ● Solve word problems involving numbers.	● **Use all four operations to solve word problems involving numbers and quantities** based on 'real life', money and measures.	
8 Multiple lines	● Recognise multiples of 2, 3, 4, 5 and 10 up to the tenth multiple.	● Recognise multiples of 6, 7, 8, and 9 up to the tenth multiple.	
9 Fill the gaps	● Recognise and extend number sequences formed by counting from any number in steps of a constant size.	● Recognise and extend number sequences formed by counting from any number in steps of any size.	
10 Grids	● Use pencil and paper methods to support, record or explain multiplications and divisions.	● Use informal pencil and paper methods to support, record or explain multiplications and divisions. ● Extend written methods to HTU or U.t × U, or TU × TU..	● Use informal pencil and paper methods to support, record or explain multiplications and divisions. ● Extend written methods to ThHTU x U.
11 Powers of ten	● Partition numbers into thousands, hundreds, tens and ones. ● Multiply and divide any positive whole number up to 1000 by 10 (whole-number answers) and understand the effect.	● **Multiply and divide any positive integer up to 10 000 by 10 or 100 and understand the effect.**	● **Multiply and divide decimals mentally by 10 or 100 and integers by 1000, and explain the effect.**
12 Factors and mulitples	● Recognise multiples of 2, 3, 4, 5 and 10 up to the tenth multiple.	● Find all the pairs of factors of any number to 100. ● Recognise multiples of 6, 7, 8 and 9 up to the tenth multiple.	● Recognise multiples of 6, 7, 8 and 9 up to the tenth multiple.
13 Target numbers	● Extend understanding of the operations × and ÷ and their relationship to each other and to + and -. Understand the principles (not the names) of the commutative, associate and distributive laws as they apply to multiplication. ● Partition e.g. (23 × 6 = (20 × 6)+(3 × 6))	● Understand and use the relationships between the four operations, and the principles (not the names) of the arithmetic laws. Use brackets.	● Understand and use the relationships between the four operations, and the principles (not the names) of the arithmetic laws. Use brackets.

Title of lesson	Tracking back Year 4 objectives	Year 5 objectives	Tracking forwards Year 6 objectives
14 Logical numbers	● Solve mathematical problems or puzzles, recognise and explain patterns, generalise and predict.	● Solve mathematical problems or puzzles, recognise and explain patterns, generalise and predict.	● Recognise squares of numbers to at least 12 × 12.
15 Fractions groups	● Use fraction notation. **Recognise simple fractions that are several parts of a whole, and mixed numbers**. ● Find fractions of shapes.	● Recognise when two simple fractions are equivalent, including relating hundredths to tenths.	
16 Measure for measure	● Know and use the relationships between familiar units.	● Use, read and write standard metric units.	● Use, read and write standard metric units.
17 Measuring up	● Use all four operations to solve word problems involving measures.	● **Solve simple word problems involving numbers,** based on measures, **explaining methods and reasoning.**	● **Identify and use appropriate operations to solve word problems involving numbers and quantities, and explain methods and reasoning.**
18 Food for thought	● Suggest suitable units and equipment to estimate or measure mass. ● **Know and use the relationships between familiar units of mass.** ● Know the equivalent of one half, one quarter, three quarters and one tenth of 1kg in grams**.**	● Use, read and write standard metric units. ● Convert larger to smaller units of mass and vice versa.. ● Suggest suitable units and equipment to estimate or measure mass.	● Use, read and write standard metric units ● Convert larger to smaller units of mass and vice versa.. ● Suggest suitable units and equipment to estimate or measure mass.
19 Decimal conversion		● **Use decimal notation for tenths, and hundredths.**	● Use decimal notation for tenths and hundredths in calculations and when recording measurements.
20 In a spin		● Discuss the chance or likelihood of particular events.	● Use the language associated with probability to discuss events, including those with equally likely outcomes.
21 Reading scales	● Record estimates and readings from scales to a suitable degree of accuracy.	● Record estimates and readings from scales to a suitable degree of accuracy.	● Convert smaller to larger units and vice versa. ● Know appropriate imperial units.
22 Everything in proportion	● **Know and use the relationship between familiar units of mass.**	● Use, read and write standard metric units including their abbreviations, and know the relationships between them.	● Use, read and write standard metric units including their abbreviations, and know the relationships between them.
23 Calendars	● Read simple timetables and use this year's calender.	● **Use all four operations to solve simple word problems involving numbers and quantities** based on 'real life', **including time.**	● **Explain methods and reasoning.**
24 Stopping distances	● Solve a given problem by representing and interpreting data in bar charts –intervals labelled in10s.	● Represent and interpret data in charts.	● Solve a problem by (representing) extracting and interpreting information presented in charts.
25 Tricky grids	● Understand the use of x and ÷ and their relationship to each other. ● Recognise multiples in the 2, 3, 4, 5 and 10 times tables and know some tests of divisibility.	● Understand the use of x and ÷ and their relationship to each other. ● Recognise multiples in the 6, 7, 8, and 9 times tables.	● Understand the use of x and ÷ and their relationship to each other. ● Recognise multiples in the 6, 7, 8, and 9 times tables.
26 Three-cornered search	● Describe and visualize 3-D and 2-D shapes. Recognise equilateral and isosceles triangles. ● **Classify polygons using criteria such as number of right angles, whether or not they are regular, symmetry properites.**	● Classify triangles (isosceles, equilateral, scalene) using criteria lines of symmetry.	

Title of lesson	Tracking back Year 4 objectives	Year 5 objectives	Tracking forwards Year 6 objectives
27 Magic crosses	● Solve mathematical problems or puzzles, recognise and explain patterns and relationships; generalise and predict.	● Solve mathematical problems or puzzles, recognise and explain patterns and relationships; generalise and predict.	● Solve mathematical problems or puzzles, recognise and explain patterns and relationships; generalise and predict.
28 Magic squares	● Solve mathematical problems or puzzles, recognise and explain patterns and relationships; generalise and predict. ● Recognise odd and even numbers up to 1000, and some of their properties.	● Solve mathematical problems or puzzles, recognise and explain patterns and relationships; generalise and predict. ● Make general statements about odd and even numbers.	● Solve mathematical problems or puzzles, recognise and explain patterns and relationships; generalise and predict. ● Make general statements about odd and even numbers.
29 Divide it up	● Begin to relate fractions to division. Use fraction notification. ● **Recognise the equivalence of simple fractions.**	● **Relate fractions to division.**	● **Use a fraction as an operator to find fractions of numbers or quantities.**
30 Make 1001	● Estimate and check by approximating. Check with an equivalent calculation.	● Check with the inverse operation when using a calculator. Estimate by approximating, then check result. ● Develop calculator skills and use a calculator effectively	● Develop calculator skills and use a calculator effectively.
31 Ratio	● Begin to use ideas of simple proportion.	● Solve simple problems using ideas of ratio and proportion.	● **Solve simple problems involving ratio and proportion.**
32 Around the pitch	● Measure and calculate the perimeter of rectangles.	● Understand, measure and calculate perimeters of rectangles.	● **Calculate the perimeter of simple compound shapes that can be split into rectangles.**
33 Net me a cube	● Make shapes and discuss properties.	● Visualise 3-D shapes from 2-D drawings and identify different nets. ● Make shapes with increasing accuracy.	● Visualise 3-D shapes from 2-D drawings and identify different nets. ● Make shapes with increasing accuracy.
34 Missing numbers	● Partition numbers into hundreds, tens and ones.	● Explain methods and reasoning orally and in writing.	● Understand and use the relationship between the four operations.
35 East to west	● Use all four operations to solve word problems involving time.	● Use all four operations to solve word problems involving time. ● Read the time on 24-hour digital clock. Use timetables.	
36 Reflections	● Sketch reflection of simple shape in a mirror line.	● Recognise reflective symmetry in regular polygons.	● Complete symmetrical patterns with two lines of symmetry at right angles.
37 Co-ordinates	● Describe and find the position of a point on a grid where the lines are numbered.	● Read and plot co-ordinates in the first quadrant.	● **Read and plot co-ordinates in all four quadrants.**
38 Pyramid puzzle	● Solve mathematical problems or puzzles, recognise and explain patterns and relationships. ● Explain methods and reasoning about numbers orally and in writing. ● Check by using the inverse operation.	● Solve mathematical problems or puzzles, recognise and explain patterns and relationships. ● Explain methods and reasoning about numbers orally and in writing. ● Check by using the inverse operation.	● Solve mathematical problems or puzzles, recognise and explain patterns and relationships. ● Explain methods and reasoning about numbers orally and in writing. ● Check by using the inverse operation.
39 Area	● Measure and calculate the area of rectangles and other simple shapes, using counting methods and standard units.	● **Understand area measured in square centimetres; understand and use the formula in words 'length × breadth' for the area of a rectangle.**	

Title of lesson	Tracking back Year 4 objectives	Year 5 objectives	Tracking forwards Year 6 objectives
40 Sorting quadrilaterals	● **Classify polygons using criteria such as number of right angles, whether or not they are regular, symmetry properties.**	● Recognise reflective symmetry in 2-D shapes. ● Identify, estimate and order acute and obtuse angles.	● Identify, estimate and order acute and obtuse angles.
41 Planning a party	● **Choose and use appropriate number operations and ways of calculating to solve problems.** ● Solve word problems involving money. ● Explain methods and reasoning about numbers orally and in writing.	● **Use all four operations to solve simple word problems.** ● Develop calculator skills and use a calculator effectively.	● Use all four operations to solve money or 'real life' word problems. ● Develop calculator skills and use a calculator effectively.
42 What comes next?	● Recognise and extend number sequences formed by counting from any number in steps of constant size.	● Explain a generalised relationship (formula) in words.	● Recognise and extend number sequences.
43 An unfair spinner	● Solve a given problem by collecting data in tally charts.	● Solve a problem by representing, extracting and interpreting data in tables, charts, graphs and diagram.	● **Solve a problem by** (representing), **and interpreting data in tables, graphs, and charts.**
44 Make 15	● Solve mathematical problems or puzzles, recognise and explain patterns and relationships; generalise and predict. ● Recognise odd and even numbers.	● Solve mathematical problems or puzzles, recognise and explain patterns and relationships; generalise and predict. ● Make general statements about odd and even numbers.	● Solve mathematical problems or puzzles, recognise and explain patterns and relationships; generalise and predict. ● Make general statements about odd and even numbers.
45 Triangle number puzzles	● Solve mathematical problems or puzzles, recognise and explain patterns and relationships; generalise and predict.	● Solve mathematical problems or puzzles, recognise and explain patterns and relationships; generalise and predict.	● Solve mathematical problems or puzzles and explain patterns and relationships. Explain methods and reasoning about numbers orally and in writing.
43 Square number puzzles	● Solve mathematical problems or puzzles, recognise and explain patterns and relationships; generalise and predict.	● Solve mathematical problems or puzzles, recognise and explain patterns and relationships; generalise and predict.	● Solve mathematical problems or puzzles, recognise and explain patterns and relationships; generalise and predict.
47 Pentominoes	● Solve mathematical problems or puzzles, recognise and explain patterns and relationships; generalise and predict.	● Solve mathematical problems or puzzles, recognise and explain patterns and relationships; generalise and predict.	● Solve mathematical problems or puzzles, recognise and explain patterns and relationships; generalise and predict.
48 What's at the zoo?	● Solve mathematical problems or puzzles, recognise and explain patterns and relationships; generalise and predict.	● Solve mathematical problems or puzzles, recognise and explain patterns and relationships; generalise and predict.	● Solve mathematical problems or puzzles, recognise and explain patterns and relationships; generalise and predict.
49 Tangrams	● Solve mathematical problems or puzzles, recognise and explain patterns and relationships; generalise and predict.	● Solve mathematical problems or puzzles, recognise and explain patterns and relationships; generalise and predict.	● Solve mathematical problems or puzzles, recognise and explain patterns and relationships; generalise and predict.
50 Counter games	● Solve mathematical problems or puzzles, recognise and explain patterns and relationships; generalise and predict.	● Solve mathematical problems or puzzles, recognise and explain patterns and relationships; generalise and predict.	● Solve mathematical problems or puzzles, recognise and explain patterns and relationships; generalise and predict.

Mental Maths starters

1 Write my number

Learning objective
(Y4) Read and write numbers in words to 1000.

You will need
Individual whiteboards; pens and erasers.

What to do
- Write a two-digit number on the board and ask the children to write it in words.
- Repeat for a range of three-digit numbers including those with zero in the 'tens' position, and those such as 413, which end in a 'teens' number.
- For older children, repeat with four-digit numbers, including some with zero place-holders.

Target questions
- What number is ten more than ...?
- What number is 100 less than ...?

2 What's my number?

Learning objective
(Y4) Say the number names to at least 10000.

You will need
Number lines from 0 to 1000, and from 0 to 10000; markers to record progress.

What to do
- Tell the group that you are thinking of a number between zero and 1000 for them to guess. Say: *You may only answer 'higher' or 'lower' to any suggestion.*
- Take a guess from a child and mark the appropriate space on the number line. As guesses are taken, refine the search down with markers to give the lowest and highest extremes of the number range. Encourage the use of full sentences with precise mathematical language.
- Repeat the activity, but encourage the children to improve on the number of guesses made. Continue with a number line from 0 to 10000.

Target questions
- Can you find a good strategy for getting the answer quickly?
- What would be a 'better' word than bigger?

3 Get in order

Learning objective
(Y4) Order two-digit and three-digit numbers.

You will need
Two sets of 0-9 number cards.

What to do
- Organise a group of about five or six children. Shuffle and deal two sets of number cards, until each child has three cards. Keep the remainder of the cards.
- Ask the children to make a three-digit number from their cards and then to assemble themselves in order. The person with the lowest number raises their hand.
- Time the group and repeat with other groups of the same size. If you prefer a more hectic alternative, divide the class into two and pass out three sets of number cards to each group. Each group shares its cards until all are dealt, then assembles in order.

Target question
- Does your choice of number help your group? How?

Learning objective
(Y4) To order four-digit numbers.

You will need
Sets of 0-9 number cards.

4 Find me a number

What to do

● Call out a four-digit number and ask the children to make this number with their cards and then to hold it up.

● Now ask the children to select the numbers 2, 3, 5, and 7. Say: *Make the largest four-digit number you can. Read it out to me.*

● Ask the children for four-digit numbers with a range of specific properties. For example: a number between 3000 and 4000; an even number above 8000; a multiple of ten which has a three in it; the number closest to 5000; the number furthest from 5000; a multiple of three.

Target questions

● Give me a number you cannot make. Why not?

● What is the smallest four-digit number you can make? (The zero cannot go at the front.)

Learning objective
(Y5) To add mentally two three-digit numbers ending in zero.

You will need
Individual whiteboards; pens and erasers.

5 In your heads

What to do

● Read out addition questions, such as: *Two hundred and thirty plus one hundred and fifty.* Each question must be a multiple of ten to enable all the children to work out the answers mentally. Ask the children to write the answers on their board - with no written working out allowed!

● Vary the language to include *find the sum of ...* and, *add ...*

● Monitor for errors and misconceptions, and for children copying the answers of another child.

● Choose two three-digit numbers, such as 260 + 370, which bridge through a 'hundreds' barrier.

● Finish with one or two three-digit numbers that exceed 1000.

Target question

● How did you work out the answer in your head?

Learning objective
(Y4) Count on and back in steps of 100, 10 and 1 from any three-digit number.

You will need
Board pen.

6 Count on and back

What to do

● Write a three-digit number on the board. With the children, count on in steps of 100 until you pass 1000. With the same number, count on and back in steps of ten.

● Repeat with a number which has a zero place-holder in the 'tens' position.

● Start with a large three-digit number and count back in steps of 100. Count forward in tens until you pass 1000.

Target questions

● Which type of numbers are most difficult to work out when counting on? Why is this?

7 How much is that?

Learning objective
(Y4) To perform addition calculations involving money and to write money notation correctly.

You will need
Individual whiteboards; pens and erasers.

What to do
● Draw a few simple objects on the board, and include the prices (at least one object below £1.00 and one above it). Keep the amounts simple to work with mentally.
● Give the children simple addition problems to work out mentally, such as: *How much is it if I buy the pen and the book?* Ask the children to record the answers on their whiteboards and to hold them up.
● Note whether children are using the correct notation. For example, 125p or £1.25 but not £1.25p.

Target questions
● What is the difference between the prices of ... and ...?
● Why is it sometimes difficult to read money values? (The symbol sometimes comes before the number and sometimes after it.)

8 Which table is this?

Learning objective
(Y5) Know by heart all multiplication facts up to 10 × 10.

You will need
Board pen; large lined paper or exercise books.

What to do
● Write the number 36 on the board.
● Ask the children which of the tables (six, seven, eight and nine) this number is taken from. Repeat for other numbers such as 42, 54, 56 and 72.
● Ask the children to create a mini table grid, with 6, 7, 8 and 9 along each edge (see Figure 1). This mini grid contains nearly all of the difficult examples to remember from the multiplication tables.

	6	7	8	9
9	54	63	72	81
8	48	56	64	72
7	42	49	56	63
6	36	42	48	54

Figure 1

Target questions
● What can you say about the bottom left half of the table? (It is the same as the top right half because multiplication is commutative.)
● Which answers do you find 'hard'?

9 Count in steps

Learning objective
(Y5) Count in multiples of any single-digit number, starting at any two-digit number.

You will need
Board pen.

What to do
● Write a two-digit and single-digit number on the board, such as 32 and 5.
● Ask the children to count out a sequence from 32 in steps of five (stop at about 100).
● Count back again. Count back beyond 32 and down to two.
● Count down from 32 in steps of six (stop before the number becomes negative).
● Repeat with other numbers. Trace a sequence on a number line as you call out each number.
● Try counting on in steps of nine from eight.

Target questions
● What patterns are there in the numbers?
● Which sequences do you find difficult? Why?

10 Multiply and divide by ten and 100

Learning objectives
(Y5) To multiply any two-digit number by 10 and 100; to divide any three-digit number (ending in zero) by 10; and any four-digit number (ending in two zeros) by 100.

You will need
Place-value cards.

What to do
● Call out a two-digit number and ask the children to multiply it by ten in their heads, and show you the answer with place-value cards.
● Repeat with other numbers including some 'teens' numbers.
● Repeat the process, but divide three-digit numbers ending in zero, by ten.
● Now try multiplying by 100 and dividing four-digit numbers ending in two zeros, by ten.
● Illustrate the process in both directions with a place-value chart or by drawing a standard HTU table.

Target questions
● What happens if I multiply 104 by ten?
● What happens if I multiple 6.5 by ten?

11 Big numbers

Learning objective
(Y5) To practise and consolidate saying large numbers.

You will need
Individual whiteboards; pens and erasers.

What to do
● Write the number 4 217 on the board.
● Ask the children to copy the number onto their whiteboards and to 'speak it in their heads'.
● Ask a child to read the number back to you.
● Repeat with harder numbers such as 3 017 and 4 006.
● Repeat this process with first five-, and then six-digit numbers. Remember to put spaces between groups of three digits.
● Build up the sequence 1, 21, 321, 4 321, 54 321, 654 321 and 7 654 321. Ask the children to read the numbers back to you. Choosing a sequence such as this reinforces the vocabulary and the place value.

Target question
● Who can write and say an eight-digit number?

12 Factor bugs

Learning objective
(Y5) To find factors of two-digit and three-digit numbers with a calculator.

You will need
Calculators.

What to do
● Write in the centre of the board a composite number (one which is not prime) such as 36, and put a loop around it.
● Tell the children that this is the body of a 'factor bug'. The number one and 36 can be used as the 'feelers' on the 'factor bug', and its 'legs' will be made from the factors.
● Ask the children for any factor of 36 (in their heads). Take the answer and draw a 'leg' for the 'factor bug' from the body to this factor. Ask for more legs to the 'factor bug' until all have been found.
● Repeat with a more demanding number, such as 144, but allow the children to use calculators.

Target question
● What is special about factor bugs with no 'legs'? (They are prime numbers - with only two factors, 'one and themselves'.)

<table>
<tr><td>

Learning objective
(Y6) To determine which mathematical operation has been performed, to get an answer.

</td></tr>
</table>

13 Missing signs

What to do

● Write on the board 2 __ 3 __ 4 = 14
● Say to the children that there are two operation signs missing from this number sentence. Can they work out what they are?
● Repeat with (2 __3) __4 = 20 (the same operations are used but the order is changed by the brackets).
● Repeat with each of the examples below (which illustrate the distributive law through the use of brackets to alter the results of a calculation). The symbols used are the same for each pair.

You will need
Board pen.

7 __ (5 __ 3) = 14	7 __ 5 __ 3 = 32
7 __ (5 __ 3) = 22	(7 __ 5) __ 3 = 36
7 __ (5 __ 3) = -1	7 __ 5 __ 3 = 9

Target question

● What happens to the calculation when we use brackets?

Learning objective
(Y6) To interpret spoken problems involving two or more steps of reasoning.

14 Number detective

What to do

● Take one number card, for example 3, hold it up facing you and say: *This number is odd and a factor of 12.* The children write the answer on their whiteboards and hold it up.
● Discuss the responses and tackle any misconceptions at once.
● Repeat with other single digits. Vary the number properties used – include factors, multiples and prime numbers when the children are confident with these.
● Now take two single-digit cards, for example, 4 and 8, and say to the children: *One number is double the other.* Continue with: *The larger number is four more than the smaller number.*

You will need
Individual whiteboards; pens and erasers; one set of 0-9 number cards.

Target question

● What numbers could be in my hand? (Ask them to make a list and eliminate those that are not possible.)

Learning objective
(Y4) To create and recognise fractions equivalent to one half.

15 It's always a half

What to do

● Draw a 2 × 3 rectangle on the board and draw in the six small squares. Ask the children how they could divide it in half. Discuss the straightforward way of doing this and ask: *Can we see that it is one half from the small squares?*
● Discuss the equivalence of $\frac{3}{6}$ (from three of the six squares shaded) and $\frac{1}{2}$.
● Ask the children to draw your rectangle and to illustrate one half a different way. Discuss the variety of ways of doing this, but point out that they all show that $\frac{3}{6}$ is equivalent to $\frac{1}{2}$.
● Ask the children to draw another rectangle of their own choosing and to shade one half in an interesting way. Ask each child to write the

You will need
Individual whiteboards; pens and erasers.

equivalent fraction for one half of their rectangle on their boards and to hold it up for everyone to see.
- Make a list of all of the equivalent fractions on the board.

Target questions
- What do you notice about all of these fractions?
- Were there any rectangles that you found difficult? (If both sides are an odd length, such as 5 × 3, then there will be a discussion about whether such things as $7\frac{1}{2}$ / 15 are the same as one half.)

16 How tall am I?

Learning objective
(Y5) To measure heights using graph paper. Explain methods and reasoning.

You will need
Cut-up strips of graph paper (or squared paper) 20cm × 5cm (one for each pair of children).

What to do
- Group the children into pairs. Tell them that each of them is to measure the height of their partners, using only the graph paper. They must discuss an efficient way of doing this as accurately as possible.
- If the children need a prompt, then tell them that five lengths of the longer side make one metre.

Target questions
- Did you use both lengths of the graph paper?
- In what units was your answer? Why did you use this unit?

17 How long is a piece of string?

Learning objective
(Y4) To estimate and then measure the length of a piece of string.

You will need
Lengths of string all the same length (approximately one metre); small pieces of tape or Blu-Tack; rulers.

What to do
- Stick each length of string to the table – one piece for each pair of children – making sure it follows an irregular series of loops.
- The children can touch the string, but they cannot move it from the table.
- In pairs they must estimate its length 'by eye'.
- Once an estimate has been agreed they must try to measure its length, again without moving it. They are allowed to use a ruler.
- Finally they should un-stick the string and measure it again.

Target question
- What strategies did you use to help you to estimate or measure its length?

18 Odd one out

Learning objective
(Y5) To use estimation to determine which of several packets is the odd one out.

You will need
Several small packets of food with masses ranging from 100g to 500g; small 100g or 200g weights.

What to do
- Open each packet. Place small weights in a few of them (enough to increase the weight of a packet by about half). Reseal the packets. To make the activity more difficult, remove some contents of packets to make them lighter.
- Explain to the children that they are to discover which packets show the incorrect mass. Find the 'odd one out' by estimation, balancing in the hand, and discussion.

Target question
- Were any of the masses more difficult to identify than others?

19 Decimal conversion

Learning objective
(Y4) To convert metres and centimetres, pennies and pounds, and to use the correct notation.

You will need
Individual whiteboards; pens and erasers.

What to do
● Write on the board: *I am 1.65m tall* (or whatever is appropriate). Ask the children to convert this height into centimetres and to write it in full on their boards. When they hold their boards up, monitor them for errors and misconceptions.
● Repeat with other lengths, converting to and from metres to centimetres, including lengths such as 102cm.
● Write a price on the board, such as £2.34. Ask the children to convert it to pence and to write it in full.
● When they hold up their boards, monitor them for errors and misconceptions. In particular make sure children do not write £234 or 2.34p or some other incorrect notation.
● Ask for other conversions from pence into pounds, including some that involve zeros.

Target questions
● How do we say 154cm in metres? (Check that the children say correctly, *One point five four metres*.)
● How do we say 154 pence in pounds? (Check that children say correctly, *One pound fifty four pence*.)

20 Spinners

Learning objective
(Y6) Use the language associated with probability.

You will need
A copy of the interactive teaching program (ITP) called 'Number Spinners'. This is available from the Standards website. It is currently at http://www.standards.dfes. gov.uk/primary/ teachingresources/ mathematics/nns_itps

What to do
● Click on the triangle icon to create a spinner. Click on its centre to spin it. Click on a number in the spinner to increment it.
● Make a spinner with two numbers the same, such as 3, 3, 4. Ask the children which number is more likely to come up. Discuss the replies.
● Alter the spinner to have five sides with the numbers 6, 6, 1, 1, 3. Ask which number is more likely to come up. Discuss the replies.
● Give the spinner six sides and the numbers 1 to 6. Ask the children how they might use this spinner (make sure that the children realise that this is the same as a normal dice).
● Explore two and three spinners.

Target questions
● What number is more/less likely to come up?
● Give me a number which is impossible!
● How can I create a spinner which gives me a result which is certain?

21 Reading scales

Learning objective
(Y4) To read and interpret scales.

What to do
● Place a weight or two on the scales by clicking a + sign. Click a - sign to remove a weight.
● Alter the maximum mark to 100 and place some weights on the scale. Ask the children to read the scale.
● Say: *If I take off the 20g weight, what will be the reading on the scale?*

You will need
A copy of the interactive teaching program (ITP) called 'Measuring scales'. This is available from the Standards website. It is currently at the address below:
http://www.standards.dfes. gov.uk/primary/ teachingresources/ mathematics/nns_itps

● Increase the maximum reading to 500 and repeat the activity.
● Reset the program and click on the small red arrow on the scales until the dial moves around to, say, 385g. Click the large black dot to reveal a digital readout of the weight.
● Ask the children for the smallest combination of weights needed to achieve this reading.

Target questions
● What will happen if I place (remove) this weight?
● What is the value of this mark (between two labelled values)?

22 Half as much again

What to do
● Tell the children that you are going to write a number on the board and they must halve it in their heads. Write 24 on the board, with the children's answer on the right, next to it.
● Now tell the children to add the half of 24 on to 24. Obtain the answer from the children and write this next to both the 24 and the 12.
● Explain that you are going to give some more numbers – the children must halve each new number and add this on to the original number. Point out that this process is sometimes called, 'finding half as much again'.
● Continue with straightforward numbers, such as 40, and then some more demanding ones, such as 68.

Learning objective
(Y5) To calculate mentally half of a number and then to add this value to the original number.

You will need
Board pen and wiper.

Target questions
● What strategy are you using to help you with this problem?
● Which numbers are easy to work out and which ones are more difficult?

23 I need a date!

Learning objective
(Y5) To calculate dates or days using information about 'today'.

What to do
● Ask the children for today's day and date. Invite them to work out what the date will be on Saturday (or another day).
● Ask the children what day a particular date falls on (about a week ahead). Show them on the calendar.
● Continue with questions related to finding days and dates up to a week or two ahead or in the past.
● Ask the children how many days there are in this month. Ask: *What day is the first of next month?* Go through the calculation by counting on in sevens to the end of the month.
● Use a calendar to illustrate the structure of a month.

You will need
A large calendar: you might like to use one on a computer.

Target questions
● Are there any strategies or shortcuts which will help us with the calculations?
● How can I quickly work out the date for the same day as today but next week?

🔲 **17**

Learning objective
(Y4) To interpret data set out in a number of ways.

You will need
A computer with a spreadsheet to display some data as a stacked bar chart.

24 Staying for lunch

What to do

● Tell the children that the numbers of boys and girls wanting a school lunch were recorded each day for a week.

● Type this table of data into a spreadsheet as the children watch.

	Mon	Tues	Wed	Thur	Fri
Girls	10	12	8	9	7
Boys	5	7	4	10	7

● Select all of the data, including the heading. Choose the graphing option for a stacked bar chart. This will illustrate the boys and girls for each day as just one bar with two different coloured sections.

● Ask questions about the data, for example: *Which day was most popular with the girls?*

● Invite the children to comment on the positive and negative aspects of illustrating data in this way.

Target questions

● Can you tell 'at a glance' whether more boys or more girls stayed for lunch that week?

● If half the girls on Monday changed their mind, what would the bars look like for that day?

Learning objective
(Y5) To understand the use of multiplication and division, and their relationship to each other.

You will need
Individual whiteboards, pens and erasers for each child.

25 Think of a question

What to do

● Write a number, such as 12, on the main board. Tell the children that this is the answer to a problem involving multiplication or division.

● Ask the children to write a calculation for which 12 is the answer, and to hold up their questions. Discuss the various 'solutions' and pick one of the less straightforward examples.

● Ask the children to write two more calculations with the numbers 6, 12 and 72.

● Discuss the results and emphasise the relationships between the numbers.

● Write the number 20 on the board and ask the children to write three related questions involving the number 20.

● Repeat for other numbers such as 56 or 63 which are 'difficult' numbers on the multiplication tables. Children who are struggling can take the 'easy' option of simply doubling or multiplying the number by ten and using that as the first part of a division calculation.

● To remind children of the relationship, try writing the numbers in a 'triangle', with the product at the top and the two divisors underneath.

Target question

● How does this relationship help us with our multiplication tables?

Learning objective
(Y4) To describe and begin to classify triangles, according to their properties.

26 What's my shape?

What to do

● Label the vertices of each shape with the letters A, B and C (and D for the quadrilaterals). Put all of the shapes into the box.

You will need
Large cut out triangles and one or two quadrilaterals; a large box or screen to hide the shapes.

● Slowly reveal one vertex of a shape to the children and ask what sort of shape it could be. Ask them what shape it could not be. Reply to suggestions from the children by asking how they know. Ask: *What is it about the shape that tells you this?*
● Lower the shape into the box and then reveal another vertex. Repeat for the third vertex. Ask the children if they are sure what sort of shape this is now.
● Repeat the activity for other shapes. Allow the children to articulate their thoughts as they build up the properties of a shape, piece by piece.

Target questions
● What properties are most useful in helping you to decide what a shape is?
● How can you tell that a shape is not a quadrilateral from its vertices?

27 Consecutive sums

Learning objective
(Y5) To understand some of the properties of consecutive numbers.

You will need
A set of 0-9 number cards for each child.

What to do
● Explain to the children what consecutive numbers are. Give several examples. Ask some children for examples of three consecutive numbers.
● Continue by asking for a list four consecutive numbers, the last of which is ten and so on.
● Ask the children to hold up two consecutive number cards which have a sum of 13. Ask the children how they worked this out. Repeat for other numbers below 18.
● Ask for a set of three consecutive numbers which add to 12. Again ask for the strategy used to find them. If the children are struggling then point out that there is a relationship between the middle number of the set of three and the sum you have asked for.

Target questions
● Give me a number which is impossible to make by adding two consecutive number cards. (Any even number.)
● Give me a number which is impossible to make by adding three consecutive number cards. (Any number not a multiple of three.)

28 Even sums

Learning objective
(Y5) Partition numbers according to given rules.

You will need
A set of 1-9 number cards for each child.

What to do
● Tell the children to take the number cards from 1 to 4 and place them into two piles so that the sum of the numbers in each pile is the same. Ask them for their solutions - there is only one way to solve this.
● Repeat using the cards 1 to 7. Again, ask for the different ways to partition the set equally. There are several ways to do this. Record the children's suggestions on the board.
● Repeat with the cards 1 to 5. This is impossible, but the aim is to allow the children time to decide this for themselves.
● Ask: *What single card can I add to the set of 1 to 5 to make the problem possible?* (Including a 7 or a 9 will each provide a variety of solutions.)

Target question
● How can you tell quickly if a number can be split equally?

Learning objectives
(Y4) To practise doubling and halving; to recognise these as inverse processes.

You will need
Board pen and wiper.

29 Think of a number

What to do
● Ask everyone to think of a number below 20.
● Say: *Double it; add ten; halve it; subtract the number you first thought of.*
● Ask the children to collectively call out their number. You should have a chorus of, *Five!*
● Repeat, with the instructions: *Double; add 12; halve; subtract six; subtract the number you first thought of.* The answer should be zero. Repeat for a few more similar chains.
● Explain how the 'magic' works by drawing a flow chart on the board to describe each step. Show the children that the second part of the calculation is the inverse of the first.

Target questions
● What happens if my starting number is zero?
● Will this work for a fraction? Let's try starting with one half.

Learning objectives
(Y5) To use a calculator effectively; to learn to adjust an answer to improve the solution to a problem.

You will need
A calculator for each child (must be four function type, not scientific); an overhead projector calculator, if available.

30 Calculator hops

What to do
● Show the children how to use the constant key. Tell them to enter the number 5 and to press + then =.
● Ask them to continue pressing the = key and to comment on what they see. (This produces the multiples of five.) Repeat for another multiple.
● Now show the children how to start from, say, three, and then add fives (type 3 + 5 =, =, =... to get the sequence 3, 8, 13, 18, 23, 28 ...).
● Explain that this is a mini investigation. They must start with any number below ten and they can add any multiples of any number they like below ten. They must 'land' exactly on 30.
● Together find, for example, 3 + 9 + 9 + 9 = 30. Find as many ways to do this as possible. As the children suggest them, write them on the board for others to check.
● If the children are confident, or you are trying this for the second time, then go for a larger target, and allow them to count on in larger steps. Some children may also explore starting with the target and working back.

Target questions
● What is the smallest number of steps you need?
● What is the largest number?

Learning objective
(Y6) Solve simple problems involving ratio and proportion.

31 Two for you and one for me

What to do
● Organise the children into pairs. Ask one from each pair to take 15 cubes or counters.
● Ask one of each pair to share the counters using the rule: 'Two for you and one for me'. The person sharing must start by giving two to

You will need
Cubes or counters.

their partner and finish by giving themselves one.
● Ask: *Did anyone have any left over?* Ask the children to explain why there is no remainder.
● Repeat the activity, using the rule: Three for you and two for me. Again discuss the lack of remainder.
● Encourage the children to see the process as repeatedly sharing out a group. If that group is a factor of the pile then there will be no remainder.
● Try this again with 24 cubes and the rule, *Four for you and two for me.*

Target question
● What other rules will leave no remainder with 24 cubes?

32 Two routes - one answer

Learning objective
(Y4) To practise doubling and adding small two-digit numbers.

You will need
Board pen and wiper.

What to do
● Write two numbers on the board such as 12 and 9. Ask the children to mentally add the two numbers and then to double the result.
● Repeat, but this time ask the children to: *Double 12 - call it out; Double 9 - call it out; add the result.*
● Allow the children to work in pairs so that each one of the pair remembers one of the doubled numbers. They can also check each other's calculations.
● Ask the children what they notice (that the answers to the first and second questions are the same).
● Repeat using the numbers 15 and 21 (or choose smaller numbers if the group need additional support).

Target questions
● Why are the answers always the same?
● What happens if we try it with two fractions, such as one half and one quarter?

33 Net of a tetrahedron

Learning objective
(Y5) To visualise how four equilateral triangles will fold to make a tetrahedron.

You will need
Four triangles which link together, such as Polydron.

What to do
● Ask the children to define a tetrahedron (a solid made from four triangles). Show them an example.
● There are two nets of a tetrahedron and a couple of others which look plausible but which do not work. Make each one and place the set for the children to see. If necessary, lay the triangles on an overhead projector, so that the shadow of the shapes is seen by all the children.
● Ask the children which arrangements will fold to make tetrahedron. They are not allowed to touch the pieces. Encourage them to discuss their ideas with each other. Fold each one up to check.

Target question
● How can we know that there are only two different nets for a tetrahedron?

Learning objective
(Y4) To know what each digit represents in a three-digit number.

You will need
Individual whiteboards, pens and wipers (or paper and pen) for each child; one set of 0-9 number cards.

A	B	C
+	D	E

34 Largest sum

What to do

● Draw a grid of boxes on the board, into which digits will be placed to represent a three-digit number being added to a two-digit number, such as that shown on the left. Ask the children to make a copy.
● Shuffle the cards and select five. Do not let the children see them.
● Tell them that you are going to call out the selected numbers, one at a time. The children must write the number you call out in one of the empty boxes.
● After all five digits have been called out the children must add the two numbers formed together. The person with the highest total is the winner.
● Repeat the game with the remaining five cards. Watch to see if the children have learned any strategies from the previous game.

Target questions

● What are good digits to place in box C or E (or other boxes)?
● What is the highest total you could get?

Learning objective
(Y5) To calculate the time interval between two given events.

You will need
Board; pen and wiper.

35 How long is that?

What to do

● Ask the children for the number of minutes in one hour, two hours, three hours and half an hour.
● Tell the children that it is 9:36am. Ask them to calculate how many minutes there are until ten o'clock. Ask: *What about eleven o'clock? How long has passed since 7 o'clock? How long since 8:15?*
● Repeat with an example based on the 24-hour clock, such as; *How many minutes are there between 14:56 and 16:03?*
● Repeat for longer time intervals or choose times which span midday.
● Conclude with: *I start my video late one night at 23:45. It stops at 02:12. How long was it recording for?*

Target question

● What is a good way of calculating minutes between say 11.46 and 12:15?

Learning objective
(Y4) To understand how an image appears when reflected in a mirror.

You will need
A copy of the interactive teaching program (ITP) called 'Symmetry'. This is available from the Standards website. It is currently at the address below.
http://www.standards.dfes.gov.uk/primary/teachingresources/mathematics/nns_itps

36 Mirror game

What to do

● Run the program and select the default vertical mirror line. Click on the left-hand side of the grid to shade a square.
● Ask a child to come to the computer and to click where they think the image of the square is in the mirror. Click on the icon to reveal the image.
● Repeat with another square or make the problem more demanding by clicking several squares to make, say, an L shape.
● If you want to run this activity as a demonstration, then click on the image yourself and ask the class as a whole if they think you are right.
● Increase the level of difficulty by repeating with a mirror line at 45°.

Target question

● What strategies are there for finding the squares in the reflected image?

37 Lost cat

What to do
- Label the x and y axes and number them from (0,0) up to (6,6).
- Tell the children that there is a cat lost on the grid. The children must try to find her by offering co-ordinates of where they think she is. Tell them that after each guess, you will help them by saying: *hot, warm* or *cold.*
- The aim is to find the cat in as few guesses as possible. So that they do not think you are 'cheating', write the co-ordinates on a piece of paper.
- Ask the children for the first guess. Assuming that someone is not very lucky, draw a cross where their guess was, write the co-ordinates on the board and write *hot, warm* or *cold* alongside.
- Continue, allowing the children to discuss and guess, until they find her.

Target questions
- What is a good strategy to use after you have a few clues in place?
- What are the best co-ordinates to start with?

Learning objective
(Y5) To understand the conventions for plotting co-ordinates and to use this knowledge to solve a problem.

You will need
A large grid of squares (about 6 × 6) on the board or on an interactive whiteboard.

38 Squares on a hundred square

What to do
- Shade the four numbers 23, 25, 43 and 45 on a hundred square. These form a small square with a gap between each number.
- Ask the children to add the two squares in opposite corners. Ask: *What do you notice?* (The opposite corners have the same sum, 68 in this case.)
- Repeat for another four squares in the same sort of pattern.
- Ask the children to try a few of their own. Is it always true that opposite corners have the same sum?
- Ask the children if they can predict what the total will be when you add the opposite corners. Direct them to look at the square in the middle. (The sum is double the middle square.)
- Repeat the exercise for other sized squares and rectangles.

Target question
- What happens to a number if I move down one square and one square to the right?

Learning objective
(Y5) Make and investigate a general statement about familiar numbers.

You will need
A hundred square for each child to write on; a large hundred square for demonstration.

39 Products

What to do
- Write a number, such as 24, on the board. Tell the children that you want to find two numbers which multiply to make 24. Remind them that this is called the product.
- Collect responses on the board in the form of 12 × 2, 6 × 4 and so on.
- Continue collecting all the combinations of two numbers that make 24. If a child does not suggest 1/2 × 48 then say: *What about trying fractions?*
- Draw the activity to a close and then change the number to 36.
- Set the children off in a mini competition to find ten products.

Target question
- How can we be systematic and make sure that we do not miss any products?

Learning objective
(Y5) To practise multiplying single-digit numbers mentally.

You will need
Board, marker and wiper.

40 Name that shape

Learning objective
(Y5) To identify and name all of the quadrilaterals.

You will need
Large cut-out quadrilaterals - square, rectangle, rhombus, parallelogram, trapezium, kite, arrowhead and one with no special properties. A large box or screen to hide the shapes.

What to do

● Label the vertices of each shape with the letters A, B, C and D. Put all of the shapes into the box. Tell the children that the box contains every sort of quadrilateral.

● Slowly reveal one vertex of a shape to the children and ask what sort of shape it could/could not be. Reply to suggestions from the children.

● Lower the shape into the box and then reveal another vertex. Repeat for the third vertex. Ask the children if they are sure what sort of shape this is now. If not, reveal the fourth vertex. Make sure the shape is named correctly before moving on.

● Avoid names such as, 'diamond' and 'oblong' in favour of the mathematical names. Remind children that a square shown 'point up' is still a square.

● Repeat the activity with other quadrilaterals.

Target questions

● What characteristics of a shape help us to name it?
● When the shape is revealed, which views of it are more helpful?

41 Calculating cash

Learning objectives
(Y5) Develop calculator skills.
(Y5) Solve simple word problems.

You will need
A calculator for each child; an overhead projector calculator, if available.

What to do

● Tell the children that they are going to find the price of some items using the calculator.

● Say: *A drink costs £1.20. How much does it cost for nine drinks?* Collect the replies from the children and interpret the answers. Some children may not understand the display of 10.8 and will misread it as 'Ten pounds eight pence'.

● Explain that the display does not show the final zero and we have to know that it is there. Say to the children: *How would I enter ten pounds and eight pence into the calculator?*

● Repeat by asking for the cost of seven drinks at £1.20.

● Alter the question and say: *I have £13.20 to spend. How many drinks can I buy?*

● Continue with: *What if I had £7.00 to spend?*

Target questions

● How do I enter 45p into the calculator, if I am working in pounds?
● How do I enter one pound seven pence into a calculator?

42 Monty

Learning objective
(Y5) Solve mathematical problems or puzzles (using ICT).

What to do

● The activity will work best if an interactive whiteboard is available. If not, run the program, click on the 'Timer' and increase the time to 30 or 40. Click on 'Start' and make sure all children can read the grid that appears on the screen.

● Give the children a short while to understand the grid. It will be a

You will need
A copy of the computer program 'Monty'. This has been sent into all primary schools in the pack entitled, *Using ICT to support mathematics in primary schools*. It is also available online from the Standards website at www.standards.d fes.gov.uk/numeracy/ publications

normal hundred square, but it is likely to have a different orientation. Click on the grid and a snake, 'Monty' (as in Monty Python!) will move around the grid. Click the grid again and he will stop.

● Invite the children to suggest numbers under 'Monty'. Enter their guesses and allow them to refine their answers until all of 'Monty' is covered.

● Repeat, but shorten the time the children see the grid, or choose another grid. The grids become much harder, quite quickly.

Target question
● What patterns in a grid help us to work out what the hidden numbers should be?

43 Mind reader?

What to do
● Give each child a dice. Tell them that you are going to influence one or two of them to throw the numbers you want. Continue by saying that you can get some people to follow your instructions several times.

● The children all start by standing up. Tell them to be careful throwing their dice.

● Call out: *Even*. Each child throws their dice. Those with even numbers remain standing and the others sit down. Call out: *Odd*. Each child throws again, and those with odd numbers remain standing – the others sit down.

● Continue with other calls which have a 50/50 chance of coming up, such as: *Numbers four and above*.

● Hopefully there will be one child remaining after several throws, who has been 'influenced' by you.

● If you have a small class, choose numbers with a higher probability, such as: *Anything above a one*.

Learning objective
(Y6) To introduce children to the idea of variation when dice are used.

You will need
One dice or a spinner for each child (it does not matter what numbers are on them providing they are the same for each child).

Target question
● Why is it that one or two people can throw what I ask them several times is a row?

Learning objective
(Y5) To recognise two- and three-digit numbers with specific properties.

You will need
One set of 0-9 number cards for each child.

44 Show me a number

What to do
● Ask the children to hold up a two-digit multiple of ten.

● Invite the children to show you a succession of numbers with specific properties. The following are suggestions, but you could adapt the questions to fit your own objectives.

● *Show me: a two-digit odd multiple of seven; a large two-digit multiple of seven; the largest two-digit multiple of three; a three-digit multiple of three; two consecutive digits which make a multiple of nine; a number which is both a multiple of three and a multiple of seven; a (large) number which is not on any of the multiplication tables (leading towards prime numbers); the smallest (largest) three-digit multiple of five.*

Target questions
● How do you know that your answer is correct? Is it the only answer?
● How can you check that your answer is the smallest (largest)?

🔲 **25**

<table>
<tr><td>

Learning objective
(Y6) To recognise two- and three-digit numbers with specific properties.

</td></tr>
</table>

45 Number pairs

What to do

● Ask the children to hold up a two-digit multiple of ten. (To let you check that all children are holding their cards the correct way round).

● The questions below demand more from the children than just answers. The restriction of using only one set of number cards means that there are significant elements of problem-solving to do as well. If the children find it hard to hold up two pairs of two-digit numbers, try the activity with children working in pairs.

● Say: *Show me a pair of ... numbers which add to 20; numbers with a product of 24; numbers with a difference of six; two-digit numbers with a difference of six; numbers which add to 100; two-digit numbers which add to 100; consecutive odd (even) numbers; two-digit consecutive odd (even) numbers; two factors of 48; two multiples of seven.*

You will need
One set of 0-9 number cards for each child.

Target questions

● How do you know that your answer is correct? Is it the only answer?
● How can you check that your answer is the smallest (largest)?

Learning objective
(Y5) Make and investigate general statements about familiar numbers.

46 Four square

What to do

● Draw a two by two grid of squares on the board. Ask the children to make a copy on paper, with squares large enough for number cards.

● What follows is a series of number puzzles. For each puzzle, tell the children to place a number card in each square, according to a rule. Examples include:

　1) Each row has an odd total, each column has an odd total and all four numbers add to ten.

　2) Each row has an odd total, each column has an odd total and all four numbers add to 30

You will need
One set of 0-9 number cards for each child; paper and pens.

Target question

● Can you find another solution with larger (smaller) numbers?

Learning objective
(Y5) Solve mathematical problems or puzzles.

47 Tetrominoes

What to do

● Tell the children that they are going to find all of the possible arrangements of joining four squares together. If they are using cut-out squares of paper, then the squares must always be joined along a full edge of each square.

● Tell the children that each arrangement must be different. For example, explain why the L shape is the same when it is flipped over.

● Ask the children to record each arrangement on squared paper. Altogether, there are five different Tetrominoes.

You will need
Each child will need either four linking squares, such as Polydron, or four squares of paper, each about 5cm × square; squared paper for recording.

Target questions

● How can we tell that we have found all of the possible arrangements?
● Where have you seen these pieces before? (The game 'Tetris'.)

48 Words

Learning objective
(Y5) To solve word problems involving two or more stages.

You will need
Paper and pencils for the children to jot notes on.

What to do

● Tell the children that you are going read aloud some short riddles. All the answers are a number.
● The riddles are:

1) Jack and Jill add their ages together and get 18. They multiply their ages together and get 80. Jack is older than Jill. How old is he?
2) Sue is twice as old as Madge. Madge is 10 years younger than Sue. How old is Madge?
3) Ali, Ben and Chris have 12 sweets between them. Ali and Ben have the same number of sweets. Chris has three more. How many does Chris have?
4) Jaz has £2 more than me, Tom has £3 less than me. We have £20 altogether. How much do I have?

Target questions

● Can you explain your working?

49 Cutting squares

Learning objective
(Y5) Solve mathematical (shape) puzzles.

You will need
Give each child a sheet with many copies of Figure 1 (see right). Alternatively, each child will need squared, or square dotty paper.

What to do

● Tell the children that they need to add lines to join the dots in order to create a variety of shapes. Show the children how to create a parallelogram and two triangles.
● Ask them to find a way to draw each of these: exactly two right-angled triangles; exactly three right-angled triangles (not all of the same size); a square and two right-angled triangles; four triangles; two trapeziums ; three triangles and an arrowhead. There are many other shapes that could be added to the list.

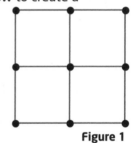

Figure 1

Target question

● Is there more than one way to find the shapes?

50 Counter lines

Learning objective
(Y4) To devise a strategy to win a game.

You will need
Six counters (three red and three blue) for each child.

What to do

● Draw a conventional noughts and crosses board. Explain to the children that they are to play a variation on this game.
● Each player places a counter on the board in turn and tries to make a line of three, as in noughts and crosses. The first move cannot be in the centre.
● If all six counters are placed and no line has been formed, then players can slide one of their counters horizontally or vertically into an empty cell.
● Play continues until one player gets three in a line. The loser starts the next game.
● Ask the children to devise a strategy for winning.

Target question

● Why is the first move not allowed to be in the centre?

Word sort

Learning objectives
(Y4) Read and write whole numbers to at least 10 000 in figures and words.
(Y5) Read and write whole numbers in figures and in words, and know what each digit represents.

Mental starter
See the starter 1 on page 10.

You will need
Individual whiteboards; pens and wipers; photocopiable page 29 for each group; sets of place-value cards to 9999.

Whole class work
● Say a three-digit number to the class. Ask the children to write it on their whiteboards and hold it up. Ask a child to read it back to the class.
● Repeat with other three-digit and four-digit numbers. Be sure to include numbers with zero as a place-holder, such as 207 or 2006.

Individual and group work
● Divide a set of 'Word sort' cards from photocopiable page 29 between a group. Challenge each child to use place-value cards to create the number in figures and record it.
● Once the children have completed the activity, ask them to work as a group to arrange all of the numbers in order.
● The word 'and' is used in numbers such as 2006. This word is often used to denote addition such as, 'three and four', as well as being used to denote an extension of a set in examples such as, 'a square and a triangle'. Children need to be taught about such language difficulties explicitly. Using a familiar number, such as a year in context, will help children to retain the place-value structure when meeting unfamiliar situations.

Plenary
● Choose a number written in words from the set and ask the children to show it to you using place-value cards.
● Say: *Show me the number that is one more/ten less/a hundred more than ...* This will help you to assess the children's understanding of place-value. (See also the lesson on page 34.)

Potential difficulties	Further support
Children are unable to find a total by counting on because they are unsure of the next number in the number sequence.	Use the place-value cards to emphasise the place-value of each digit. Set out place-value cards to show explicitly that 356 is 300 and 50 and 6. (Remind the children that place-value cards are not joined end to end, but each covers a portion of another of greater value.)
Difficulties with reading and understanding the numbers in written or word form.	Cut the photocopiable page in half down the middle. Stick one half to an A4 sheet and allow the children to write the digits alongside the written form.

Moving on
● Some children may be able to read and write numbers beyond 10 000. However, a common misconception is that ten times 10 000 is one million.
● Children are surrounded by large and often incomprehensible numbers, such as lottery winnings, football transfer fees and so on. Look out for these 'real life' examples and discuss these figures in words and digits if the opportunity arises.

Word sort

one hundred	five hundred
two thousand	nine thousand
four hundred and thirty two	six hundred and fifty two
seven hundred and four	eight hundred and one
nine hundred and ninety nine	one thousand two hundred and forty two
three thousand and six	four thousand five hundred and two
one hundred and twenty four	three hundred and forty two
one hundred and eight	five thousand two hundred and seven
six thousand and three	nine thousand nine hundred and ninety nine
one hundred and seventy	one thousand and one

Star numbers

Learning objectives
(Y4) Give one or more numbers lying between two given numbers.
(Y4) Read and write the vocabulary of comparing and ordering numbers.
(Y5) Give one or more numbers lying between two given numbers.

Mental starter
See the starter 2 on page 10.

You will need
Individual whiteboards and pens; place-value cards; 0 – 9 number cards; six or seven differently-coloured counters for each child; photocopiable page 31 for each pair.

Whole class work
● Ask the class to write *H T U* at the top of their whiteboards to represent hundreds, tens and units (ones).
● Ask them to write the number 237 in the correct position on their boards. Now ask them to write the number that is one more underneath 237, then ten more, then 100 more.
● Invite them to share their results with their partners and to discuss what they notice.
● Say: *Tell me what has changed and what stays the same, when I add first one, then ten and then 100, to 237?* Discuss the answers and make sure that the children are confident about changes to each place-value column.
● Repeat once more using the number 293 (this has the additional difficulty that adding ten crosses the 'hundreds' boundary).
● Use a similar method to practise counting back from a given number in ones, then tens and then hundreds.

Paired work
● Provide each pair with a copy of photocopiable page 31 and a set of 0 – 9 number cards. Give each child six or seven counters (a different colour each).
● Ask one child to shuffle the number cards and deal three cards each to form a three-digit number, which they place in front of them.
● The first child to identify one of the number stars that is between the two three-digit numbers 'claims it' and puts a counter over it.
● The game continues until all stars are claimed.

Plenary
● Draw a large five-pointed star on the main class board. Place a three-digit number in the centre of it.
● Ask each pair of children to select three cards from one set of cards to each make a three-digit number. One of the numbers must be smaller than your 'star number' and one must one larger.
● When ready they each hold up one of the numbers.
● Change the number and repeat.

Potential difficulties	Further support
Difficulty in discriminating all three of the digits. For example, they may not be clear that 273 is larger than 237.	Have place-value cards available at all times and allow children to use them to explore numbers.

Moving on
● Invite the children to offer a strategy for selecting their three-digit numbers. Watch for children suggesting that the way they order the digits is important when trying to maximise or minimise a number.
● Create a four-digit version of this activity.

Star numbers

126

802

198

738

209

612

921

499

873

Three in a row

Learning objectives
(Y4) Order a set of whole numbers less than 10 000.
(Y5) Order a given set of positive integers.

Mental starter
See the starter 3 on page 10.

You will need
A number stick (created by marking the back of a metre stick); small Post-it Notes; photocopiable page 33 for each pair; 0-9 number cards; felt-tipped pens.

Whole class work
- Place a Post-it Note with *0* marked on it at the end of your number stick. Add another Post-it Note with *1000* at the other end.
- Ask the children what number goes in the middle. Write *500* on a Post-it and place it in the middle. Continue with additional hundreds, such as 100 and 800, and place the numbers appropriately.
- Next, ask the children for the positions of more demanding numbers, such as 250, 750 and 50. Invite the children to explain their answers with terms such as: *It is less than 200 but more than 100* and so on.

Paired work
- Give each pair a copy of photocopiable page 33, a set of 0-9 number cards and two felt-tipped pens. Allocate one player the boxes above the number line and the other the boxes below.
- Ask the first player to select three number cards to make a three-digit number, which they enter into an empty box (the nearest box to its place on the number line) and then draw a line to the appropriate place on the number line. Finally, they place a small mark in their colour on the line and replace the cards at the bottom of the pile. Play continues with the next player.
- The aim is to get three coloured marks in a row on the number line. Once all the boxes are full the winner is the person with the most rows.

Plenary
- Draw a number line on the main class board from 3000 to 4000, mark ten divisions with vertical dashes and label the end points.
- Choose four digits to represent the thousands, hundreds, tens and units (including a '3' digit for the thousands).
- Invite a child to use these digits to make a number, write it on the board and draw a line to its position on the number line, marking the end point with a cross. Ask another child to say the number.
- Use the same digits to create a different number and mark it on the board in the same way as the children. Ask a child to say the number aloud.
- Continue until either you or the children have three marks in a row.

Potential difficulties	Further support
Numbers such as 206 may be recorded as 260.	Have place-value cards available to emphasise the place-value of each digit – for example, 206 is 200 and 6; 260 is 200 and 60.
The range of numbers is too demanding.	Alter the photocopiable sheet by replacing the final number with 100 instead of 1000.

Moving on
- Vary the activity by making the final number 10 000 and asking each child to take four-digit cards.

Three in a row

1000

500

0

Don't cross the line!

Learning objectives
(Y4) Read and write whole numbers to at least 10 000, and know what each digit represents.
(Y5) Order a given set of positive integers.

Mental starter
See the starter 4 on page 11.

You will need
Individual whiteboards and pens; photocopiable page 35 for each pair; 0 - 9 number cards and felt-tipped pens.

Whole class work

● Write four digits on the main class board. Invite the children to write four-digit numbers on their whiteboards.
● Next, invite three children to order themselves according to the numbers on their whiteboards. Ask a fourth child to join them. Continue until all the children are in the correct order.
● Repeat the activity making sure that zero is one of your chosen digits.

Paired work

● Give each pair a copy of photocopiable page 35, a set of 0 - 9 number cards and two felt-tipped pens.
● Allocate one player the boxes above the number line and the other the boxes below. Ask the children to shuffle the number cards and deal between themselves.
● Ask each player in turn to use four of the five digits cards to make a four-digit number and enter it into one of the boxes. They then draw a line to the place on the number line and place their own coloured mark on the line.
● The aim is to fill all nine boxes without any of the drawn lines crossing.
● Encourage the children to think about which box they place each number in, and how the numbers will be ordered. Working in pairs will allow the children to help each other.
● Working in pairs will allow the children to help each other, though the activity can be modified if children prefer to work alone. Ask the child to choose four digits, arrange a four-digit number and fill in a box. They continue until all 18 boxes are filled or until they are forced to make lines cross.

Plenary

● Draw a 0 to 10 000 number line on the board and mark the hundreds positions with vertical dashes.
● Choose a four-digit number. Invite a child to the board to draw a line to its position on the number line. Ask: *How do you know this number is in the correct place?* Encourage the children to explain in terms of the dashes and the size of the hundreds digit.
● Continue with other numbers. Include a number with zero in the 'hundreds' position.

Moving on
● Use number lines such as 3000 to 5000. Remind the children that the number line covers a range of 2000. Extend the set of number cards with more threes and fours, to give children more opportunities to make numbers.

Potential difficulties	Further support
Numbers such as 2061 may be recorded as 2610.	Use place-value cards to emphasise the place-value of each digit. Set out the place-value cards to show explicitly that 2061 is 2000 and 60 and 1, and that 2610 is 2000 and 600 and 10.

Don't cross the line!

A number line marked with intervals from 0 to 10000:

0

1000

2000

3000

4000

5000

6000

7000

8000

9000

10000

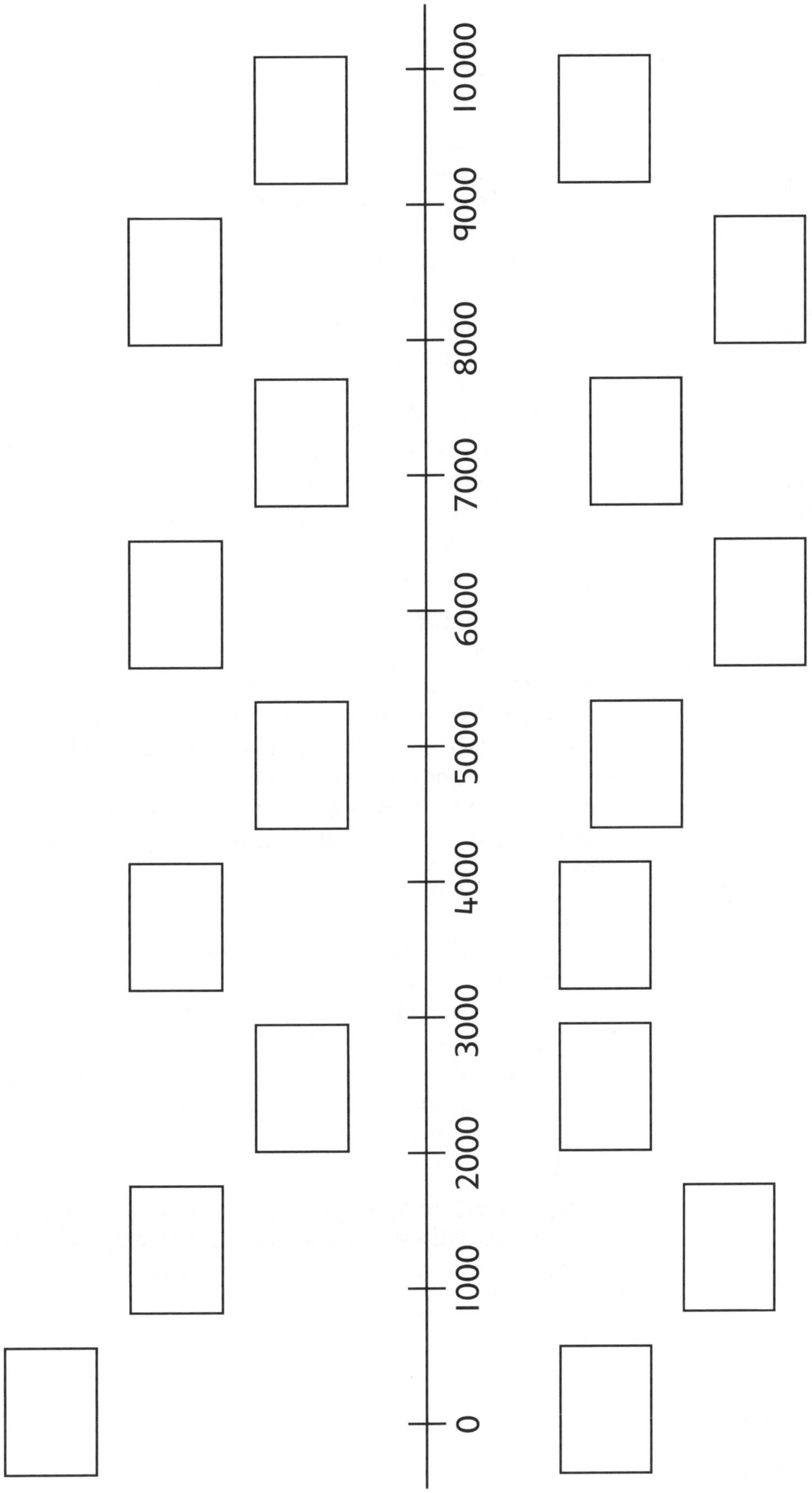

Add it on

Learning objectives
(Y4) Use informal pencil and paper methods to support additions.
(Y5) Use informal pencil and paper methods to support, record or explain additions and subtractions.

Mental starter
See the starter 5 on page 11.

You will need
Place-value cards to 999; photocopiable page 37 for each child.

Whole class work
● This activity involves encouraging the children to examine the most significant digit first, and will develop their mental strategies.
● Write the addition problem 213 + 435 on the board, set out in both horizontal and column format.
● Ask the children to display the hundreds in the answer by holding up the appropriate place-value card (600). Continue by asking for the tens and then the units or ones. Use the place-value cards to join the parts of the answer together, to complete the calculation.
● Repeat for other addition calculations and include some that cross the 'tens' boundary, such as 358 + 475. In this case, make sure that children use the place-value cards correctly. For example, when adding 358 to 475, the addition of the hundreds produces 700 and addition of the tens produces 120. (It is now common practice to refer to 'ones' rather than 'units' for consistency and clarity. However, this convention is not usually followed when setting out or discussing numbers in column format. One reason for this is that column headings would become HTO, which may be confusing for children!)

Individual work
● Give each child a copy of photocopiable page 37 and a set of place-value cards.
● Ask the children to work alone (or in pairs) to complete each calculation. Ask them first to transfer the calculation from horizontal to vertical format, and then complete the calculation by adding the hundreds, then the tens, and finally the ones (units).
● The children then add up the columns, using place-value cards to help them.

Plenary
● Repeat the whole class activity (above), this time focusing upon numbers which cross the tens boundary.
● Include some calculations such as 536 + 274 where the tens add to 100. Say: *Show me 500 plus 200 and record the answer as 700.* Then say: *Show me 30 plus 70 and record 100 underneath.* Finally say: *Show me six plus four, and record ten underneath.*
● Invite children to calculate the answer to 536 + 274 mentally, using the results collected on the board.

Potential difficulties	Further support
Children may not have the confidence to use mental strategies or may be used to always finding the ones or units first.	Encourage the children to work calculations out in their head. The point of this activity is to support mental methods, which are often best carried out from left to right, with the most significant digit calculated first.

Moving on
● Try the same activity but with four-digit numbers. Alternatively, try adding three, three-digit numbers together using the same strategy.

Add it on

236 + 352
 	
H T U
2 3 6
3 5 2
─────
5 0 0
  8 0
    8
─────
 	
─────
	235 + 454	252 + 723

416 + 242	327 + 165	516 + 348
673 + 278	477 + 566	Try one of your own.

Number line hops

Whole class work
● Write the addition problem 413 + 135 on the main class board, set out in horizontal format.
● Draw an empty number line and label 413 near the left-hand end. Draw a loop to illustrate counting on 100. Ask the children for the end point (513).
● Draw another loop to illustrate counting on three tens. Ask the children for the end point (543).
● Finally, draw a loop to illustrate counting on five and ask for the end point.

413 + 135 = 548   413 + 100 + 30 + 5

● Repeat for other addition calculations, including some that cross the 'tens' boundary.

Paired work
● Give each child a copy of photocopiable page 39. Revise the use of the empty number line.
● Invite a child to explain the first question on the activity sheet, which has been completed for them.
● Encourage the children, in pairs, to discuss the setting out of the calculation with each other.

Plenary
● It is important that children recognise the use of an empty number line as a powerful way of 'seeing' a calculation. Compare the methods of using a number line with other methods, such as column addition.
● Set up the calculation of 346 + 237 on the main board by using the number line method shown in this activity, and also by using the column method in 'Add it on' (page 36).
● Ask the children: *What is the same and what is different about the two methods?* (Both methods deal with the most significant digit first, whereas the 'traditional' addition method works with the least significant digit first.) A consequence of the traditional method is that children do not get a feel for the size of the answer and it is much more difficult for them to spot mistakes.
● Repeat, with the calculation 306 – 152, making comparisons between the use of the number line and the 'traditional' decomposition method.

Potential difficulties	Further support
Some children may find the empty number line unfamiliar.	Children will need practice with the initial concept of using a number line for addition and subtraction before using an empty number line.
Children may need support with choice of method.	Subtraction on a number line can be performed in two ways. Counting back (or taking away) from the larger number, or counting on from one number to another. In this activity the focus is on counting back.

Number line hops

◼ Carry out the addition and subtraction calculations using the number line. The first one of each type has been done for you.

147 + 38 = 185 _____

```
     +10        +10        +10        +8
  ⌢          ⌢          ⌢         ⌢
147        157        167        177      185
```

136 + 45 = _____

237 + 75 = _____

357 + 463 = _____

185 - 38 = 147 _____

```
        -8        -10        -10        -10
      ⌢          ⌢          ⌢          ⌢
    147      155        165        175        185
```

128 - 43 = _____

375 - 132 = _____

◼ Write down the calculations that these number lines show.

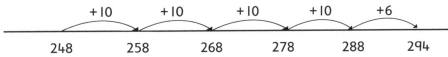

```
     +10        +10        +10        +10        +6
  ⌢          ⌢          ⌢          ⌢          ⌢
248        258        268        278        288        294
```

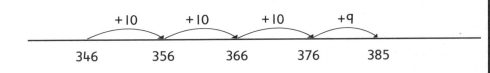

```
     +10        +10        +10        +9
  ⌢          ⌢          ⌢          ⌢
346        356        366        376        385
```

At the fairground

Learning objectives
(Y4) Choose and use appropriate number operations and ways of calculating to solve problems.
(Y4) Solve word problems involving numbers.
(Y5) Use all four operations to solve simple word problems involving numbers and quantities based on 'real life', money and measures.

Mental starter
See the starter 7 on page 12.

You will need
Photocopiable page 41 and calculators for each pair or individual.

Whole class work

● Sketch a CD, a T-shirt, a drink, sweets and a bus ticket on the main board. Attach prices to them as follows – CD: £8.50, T-shirt: £5.50 or two for £9.00, Drink: £1.50, Bus ticket: £1.20, Sweets: 60p. Explain that you have £12 to spend.

● Ask: *If I buy a T-shirt, how much change do I have left?* Ask the children to explain their answers.

● Set other problems such as: *If instead, I take up the offer of two T-shirts for £9.00 and I stop for a drink, how much do I spend?* Continue with: *Do I have enough left for sweets and a bus ticket?*

● Vary the questions and alter the amount of money available. After each problem, make sure that you ask the children to explain how they worked things out. Compare the children's methods. In particular, discuss some of the different ways of working things out in your head.

Individual and paired work

Give each child a copy of photocopiable page 41. Children can work alone on this activity, but would benefit from discussing their ideas with a partner.

● Ask the children to discuss the 'setting' suggested in the activity and make sure that they understand that they are going to use the prices given in the list to work out the costs for each person.

● Remind the children to be careful about how the prices are set out in two different ways. (Refer to the 'Further support' section below to help any children who are struggling.)

Plenary

● Use the plenary to develop another theme from the activity sheet – the friends decide to put all the money they have left together. Ask: *How much do they have left between them?*

● Suggest that the friends are going to spend the rest of the money on doughnuts. Ask the children to work out how many they can each have.

Potential difficulties	Further support
Some children will have difficulty mixing prices marked in pence with those marked in pounds. Others may calculate correctly but use incorrect notation, such as £2.45p.	Explain the conversion from pounds to pence and go over the different notation used. Convert some examples, such as 60p = £0.60.
Some children may have difficulty interpreting a calculator's displayed results.	Explain that in the context of money, 4.2 should be read as £4.20.

Moving on
● Ask the children to create their own spending list based on the prices on the activity list. Allow them £6.00 or £7.00 to spend, but insist that they account for all the money spent and calculate what they have left.

At the fairground

◖ Yasmin, Rosie, Tom and Sam are friends. Each of them has £5.00 to spend. All of the friends like the dodgems and go on this ride first, with two in each car, paying half of the cost each. They then do their favourite things. Work out how much each of them spends and what change they have left.

After the dodgems, Yasmin goes on the super slide and the waltzer and eats chips and candy floss. Work out how much Yasmin spends.

Dodgems	£0.75
Super slide	£0.60
Waltzer	_____
Chips	_____
Candy floss	_____
Total spent	_____

After the dodgems, Sam goes on the waltzer and the big wheel. He buys chips and popcorn. Work out how much Sam spends.

Dodgems	_____
Waltzer	_____
Big wheel	_____
Chips	_____
Popcorn	_____
Total spent	_____

After the dodgems, Tom goes on the super slide, the waltzer, the scary castle and the big wheel. He feels too ill to eat anything. Work out how much Tom spends.

Dodgems	_____
Super slide	_____
Waltzer	_____
Scary castle	_____
Big wheel	_____
Total spent	_____

Rides

Dodgems	£1.50 per car
Big wheel	£1.00
Super slide	60p
Scary castle	£1.00
Hook a prize	80p
Waltzer	£1.00

Mike's Food Stall

Chips	£1.00
Crisps	50p
Doughnuts	£1.00
	(bag of 4)
Candy floss	£1.20
Baked potato	£1.50
Popcorn	£0.80

◖ Work out what each person has left. Explain your calculations on the back of the page.

Multiple lines

Learning objectives
(Y4) Recognise multiples of 2, 3, 4, 5 and 10, up to the tenth multiple.
(Y5) Recognise multiples of 6, 7, 8, 9 up to the tenth multiple.

Mental starter
See the starter 8 on page 12.

You will need
0 - 9 number cards for each child; copy of photocopiable page 43 and a calculator or table square for each pair; five counters in different colours for each child.

Whole class work
● Draw a table on the board like the one shown below.
● Provide each child with a set of 0 - 9 number cards. Explain that all the numbers in a column or row (in the table) have the property of that column or row heading.

	MULTIPLE OF 2	MULTIPLE OF 7
MULTIPLE OF 3		
MULTIPLE OF 5		

● Point to a cell, and say: *Show me a two-digit number that goes in this cell. Can you explain how you know this?* Encourage answers in the form: *21 is a multiple of seven and a multiple of three.*
● Select one or two numbers from those offered and enter them into a cell. Where appropriate, demonstrate that a test of divisibility may be used to help with the calculation. Continue with the remaining cells.

Paired work
● Give each pair a copy of photocopiable page 43. Ask the children to choose Game A or Game B.
● Shuffle a set of number cards and place them face down. One player starts by taking the top two cards and trying to form a multiple of one of the numbers on the grid. If they are able, they cover it with a counter. The next player takes the next two cards and so on. If a player cannot find a multiple, they miss a turn.
● When all the cards are used, the pack is shuffled and play continues until one player has three counters in a row. In the event of no line being formed, the winner is the first player with five counters on the board. A calculator or table square may be used to help the players, or to resolve disputes or difficulties.

Plenary
● Return to the table drawn above and alter the multiples. Complete the table as before. This time ask: *Show me a number that is not in any cell.* Encourage the children to explain how they know or how they worked it out.

Moving on
● Return to the table used for the main activity above. Give children a set of 0 - 9 number cards and ask them to make four two digit numbers which will fit into the four boxes. Using only one set of number cards restricts their choice and forces them to make decisions about how best to use the cards.

Potential difficulties	Further support
Children may not be able to agree about whether a number is a multiple or not.	Demonstrate how to check using a calculator. To check that 48 is a multiple of 6, divide 48 by 6 and show that there is no remainder.

Multiple lines

Game A

multiple of 2	multiple of 3	multiple of 4
multiple of 3	multiple of 5	multiple of 3
multiple of 4	multiple of 3	multiple of 2

Game B

multiple of 2	multiple of 5	multiple of 8
multiple of 6	multiple of 7	multiple of 3
multiple of 9	multiple of 4	multiple of 2

Fill the gaps

Learning objectives
(Y4 and Y5) Recognise and extend number sequences formed by counting from any number in steps of constant size.

Mental starter
See the starter 9 on page 12.

You will need
Number lines for each child (clearly printed metre sticks may be used if appropriate number lines are not available); photocopiable page 45.

Moving on
● Challenge the children with two sequences that require some imagination. The first is the Fibonacci Sequence which begins 1, 1, 2, 3, 5, 8, ... in which each new term is the sum of the previous two terms. Add additional terms to help the children. The second sequence to offer involves the use of negative numbers. Write 10, 7, 4, __, __, __. Use a number line for support.

Whole class work
● Write the following incomplete sequence on the board: 3, ___, ___, 15. Ask the children to find the missing numbers using the clue: *The gap between each of the numbers is the same.* If the children find this too difficult, provide one of the 'unknown' numbers or include 19 after 15 as an additional clue.
● Ask: *How did you work it out?* and invite the children to offer different methods. Use a number line to illustrate the jumps. Demonstrate how we can use the information that the gaps are all the same to help.
● Repeat this activity using the sequences below. Use a number line to illustrate each sequence.

0, __, __, __, 24, 30
0, __, __, __, 20
15, __, __, 9
30, __, __, __, 10

Individual and paired work
● Give each child in the pair a copy of photocopiable page 45. Encourage the children to work together, discussing each sequence, but recording their results on their own sheets.
● The 'Fill the gaps' sheet begins with sequences that increase or decrease by a constant amount, but moves on to examples that challenge the children with sequences with variable gaps. Clues have been provided for these examples.
● If time allows, give the children a chance to create their own sequences and to challenge their partners to solve them.

Plenary
● At the end of the 'Fill the gaps' activity the children were invited to create their own sequences. Try some of these out as challenges for the other children to solve.
● Review any errors or misconceptions about the sequences.

Potential difficulties	Further support
Some children may not understand that a rule is applied consistently to every term in a sequence, and that when each of the gaps is the same, this means that each jump on the number line must be the same size.	Emphasise the use of a number line to help with finding the missing numbers. The number line needs to be accurate.

Fill the gaps

■ Each gap is the same.

a) 0, 5, _____, _____, 20, 25

b) 0, _____, _____, _____, 24

c) 15, _____, _____, 6, 3

d) 30, _____, _____, _____, 21

e) 0, 1$\frac{1}{2}$, 3, _____, 6, _____, _____, 10$\frac{1}{2}$

f) _____, _____, _____, 12, _____, _____, _____, 24

g) 4, _____, _____, _____, 2

■ The gaps increase or decrease in equal steps. Use the clues to help you.

h) 3, 5, 8, 12, _____, _____, 30   The gaps increase by 1 each time.

i) 1, 4, 8, _____, _____, 26, _____   The gaps increase by 1 each time.

j) 1, 3, 7, 13, _____, _____, 43   The gaps increase by 2 each time.

k) 30, 29, 27, _____, _____, 15   The gaps decrease by 1 each time.

■ Create some sequences of your own. Leave a clue for a partner to solve your sequence.

Grids

Learning objectives
(Y4) Use informal pencil and paper methods to support, record or explain multiplications and divisions.
(Y5 and Y6) Use informal pencil and paper methods to support, record or explain multiplications and divisions. Extend written methods to: HTU or U.t × U, or TU × TU (ThHTU × U in Y6).

Mental starter
See the starter 10 on page 13.

You will need
Photocopiable page 47 for each pair or individual.

Whole class work
● The grid method of multiplication is a quite adequate and efficient 'end point' for many children. It is not necessary to develop the traditional written method, and forcing the pace may leave children without a method they feel they own and understand.
● Illustrate the grid method of multiplication with the calculation 13 × 24. Draw the first grid (Figure 1) on the board.
● Ask: *How does this diagram help us to calculate 13 × 24?* Emphasise the dimensions of the rectangle and discuss how the calculation is broken down.
● Put in the results of the calculations as shown in Figure 2.
● Explain to the children that the result, 100 + 100 + 40 = 240 is equivalent to 24 × 10, and that 30 + 30 + 12 = 72 is equivalent to 24 × 3. Repeat the above calculation with 26 × 34.

Individual and paired work
● Explain to the children that the photocopiable sheet asks them to set out the calculations using the grid method.
● Give each child a copy of the sheet. (The children can work alone on this activity, but would benefit from discussing their ideas with a partner.)
● Ask the children to complete the sheet by adding numbers into the cells on the grid and by filling the blank spaces. Check at regular intervals that the children understand the method by asking targeted questions such as: *Can you describe the method you are using?*

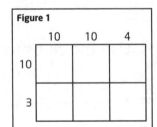

Figure 1

	10	10	4
10			
3			

Figure 2

	10	10	4
10	100	100	40
3	30	30	12

Figure 3

100 + 100 + 40	240
30 + 30 + 12	72
Total	312

Moving on
● Practise multiplying numbers such as 30 × 10, and doubling to show how to calculate 30 × 20 = 600.
● To move the class on to the point where they can set out calculations such as 68 × 56, they need to be able to understand 60 × 50 as 6 × 10 × 5 × 10 = 30 × 100 = 3000.
● Begin this process by repeating the calculation done in the whole class work but omitting the division lines separating groups of 10.

Plenary
● Use the plenary to explain and consolidate the calculations carried out on the activity sheet.
● Emphasise and explain how each of the parts of the calculation has been carried out.
● If the children have tackled the activity with confidence, then use the plenary to illustrate the calculation set out in the 'Moving on' section (left).

Potential difficulties	Further support
Children may lack confidence with the size of the numbers involved and with the intermediate processes.	To test the children's understanding, ask questions such as: *Multiply 27 by 10.* Remind the children that this calculation is the same as 20 × 10 added to 7 × 10.

Grids

■ Set out the following calculations using the grid method. Write your calculations into the boxes and spaces on the grids. The answer for the first calculation has been put in to help you.

1 Work out 15 × 23

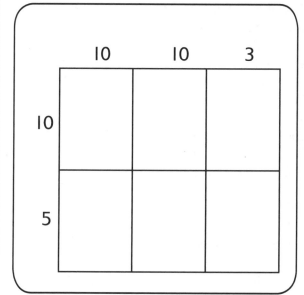

15 × 23

____ + ____ + ____ = ____

____ + ____ + ____ = ____

Total 345

2 Work out 27 × 24

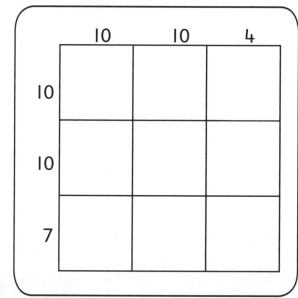

27 × 24

____ + ____ + ____ = ____

____ + ____ + ____ = ____

____ + ____ + ____ = ____

Total

3 Work out 28 × 32 by setting out the calculation on the back of this sheet.

Powers of ten

Learning objectives
(Y4) Partition numbers into thousands, hundreds, tens and ones.
(Y4) Multiply or divide any integer up to 1000 by 10 (whole-number answers) and understand the effect.
(Y5) Multiply and divide any positive integer up to 10 000 by 10 or 100 and understand the effect.
(Y6) Multiply and divide decimals mentally by 10 or 100, and integers by 1000, and explain the effect.

Mental starter
See the starter 11 on page 13.

You will need
Photocopiable page 49 for each child.

Whole class work
● Understanding the effect of multiplying or dividing by ten is an essential concept for children if they are to be confident with both place-value and calculations. When multiplying by ten it is important that children are not taught superficial rules, such as *just add a zero*, since these rules often embed misconceptions and store up problems for later.
● Write a single-digit number in the centre of the main board, such as the 5 illustrated below. Write the number in words alongside it. Ask: *What number do I get if I multiply this 5 by 10?* Write the answer *50*, above the 5 using the correct place-value. Write in the word. Continue as shown in the diagram below.

5 000 000	five million
500 000	five hundred thousand
50 000	fifty thousand
5 000	five thousand
500	five hundred
50	fifty
5	five
0.5	nought point five

● Continue this process until the children start to struggle. Emphasise the position of the digits, and that multiplying by ten moves the digits one place to the left, with a placeholder zero introduced.
● Ask additional questions such as: *How do I get from 5000 to 50?* and *What number do I get if I multiply 5 by 10 000?* Introduce the decimal number 0.5, to show that it follows the same place-value rule as the other numbers.

Individual and paired work
● Give each child a copy of photocopiable page 49. Ask the children to complete the sheet by filling numbers and words into the blank spaces. Make sure that the children understand that the direction of the arrows is important.
● Talk to the children as they work, asking them to explain what happens when you multiply by 10, or 100.

Plenary
● Use the plenary to explain and consolidate the calculations worked out on the activity sheet. Emphasise and explain how each of the parts of the calculation has been carried out.

Moving on
● Return to the decimal number introduced in the whole class work. Ask the children to create a table like the one in the diagram above, starting at 400 and repeatedly dividing by 10 until they reach 0.04. Invite the children to include the written form of the number as well.

Potential difficulties	Further support
Children often lack confidence with large numbers and may exhibit a fundamental lack of understanding of the place-value system.	It is worth pointing out to children that 0.5 × 10 = 5 and not 0.50, which they may get if they blindly follow a rule.

Name _____

Powers of ten

◼ Copy and complete the table below. Insert the numbers and words in the correct places.

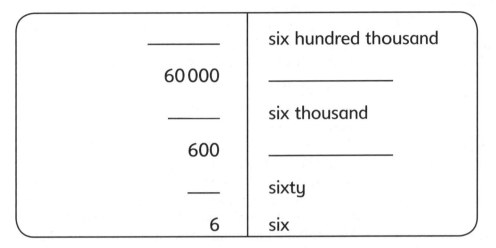

_____	six hundred thousand
60 000	_____
_____	six thousand
600	_____
_____	sixty
6	six

◼ Fill in the correct number in each box. The direction of the arrow tells you which way the calculations have been done.

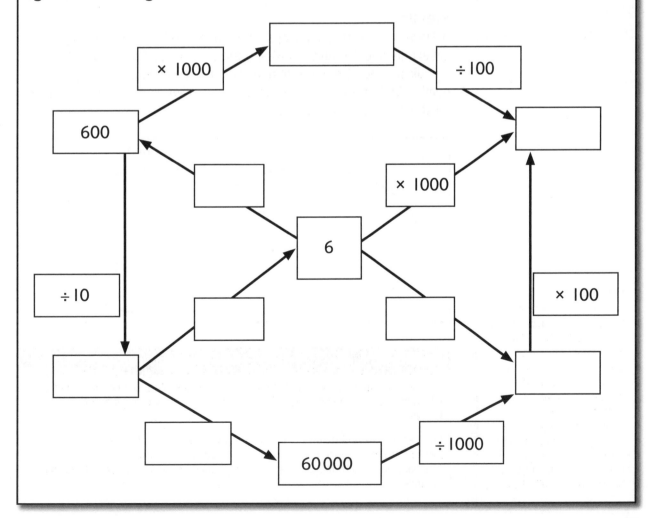

Factors and multiples

Learning objectives
(Y4) Recognise multiples of 2, 3, 4, 5 and 10, up to the tenth multiple.
(Y5) Find all the pairs of factors of any number up to 100.
(Y5 and Y6) Recognise multiples of 6, 7, 8 and 9, up to the tenth multiple.

Mental starter
See the starter 12 on page 13.

You will need
0 - 9 number cards for each group; photocopiable page 51 for each child; calculator or table square for each group.

Whole class work

● Write the number 12 on the board. Give each child a set of 0 - 9 number cards and ask them to hold up a multiple of 12.
● Discuss the various answers. If too many children show 24 then ask for another number greater than 40.
● Now say: *Show me a factor of 12.* Check that the children understand the difference between factors and multiples.
● Repeat this activity with the numbers 27 and 35.

Group work

● Give each child a copy of photocopiable page 51 and arrange the children in groups.
● Take one set of number cards and arrange them face down so that each card is accessible. Ask a child to take two cards and turn them over. Each child then uses these two digits to make a true statement, in any one of their boxes. For example, the digits 1 and 8 may be used to show that 81 is a multiple of 9, or that 18 is a factor of 36.
● The cards are turned face down again and the next player chooses two cards. Play continues until a player has completed statements in one of the four loops on the sheet. Play then continues until another loop is complete, and so on.

Plenary

● Draw two intersecting loops on the board to form a Venn Diagram. Label one loop 'Multiples of 6', and the other loop, 'Factors of 48'.
● Indicate one of the four regions and ask the children to hold up a number in that region. Place some of the answers on the board. Repeat for the other three regions.

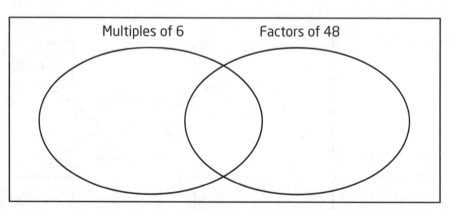

Potential difficulties	Further support
Children may struggle with multiples which are outside their immediate knowledge.	Supply a table square or a calculator. This will allow the children to focus on the strategy of the game.
Children may have difficulty with the concept of factors since far less time is usually devoted to factors than to multiples.	Practise writing down all of the factors in a given number. Remember to include both 1 and the number itself.

Moving on
● The activity with the Venn Diagram can be set up as a game for the children. They select cards in the same way as the game above, but they must get one number in each of the four cells to win.
● Allow the children to choose how many cards to turn over. They could opt for more or fewer than two if it helped them to fill a box.

Factors and multiples

	is a multiple of 2

	is a multiple of 5

	is a multiple of 10

	is a multiple of 8

	is a multiple of 3

	is a multiple of 4

	is a multiple of 6

	is a multiple of 9

	is a factor of 36

	is a factor of 60

	is a factor of 75

	is a factor of 24

	is a factor of 45

	is a factor of 100

Target numbers

Whole class work
● Check that the children are confident with partitioning and expanding numbers.
● Write 6 × 23 on the board and ask the children to calculate it mentally. Ask: *How did you work it out?* One method is likely to be 6 × 20 plus 6 × 3. Write this on the board.
● Show through discussion that 6 × 23 = (6 × 20) + (6 × 3) = 138.
● Repeat with 5 × 45.

Paired or small group work
● Give each child in the group a set of cards cut up from photocopiable page 53.
● Ask the children to decide upon a target number by taking two cards at random from a separate set of number cards and arranging them to form a two-digit number.
● Tell the children that they must make that number by using the numbers and symbols in their set - they are not allowed to put two number cards together to make a two-digit number (ensuring that more consideration is given to using the brackets).
● Explain that each card carries some points - two points for each symbol card; one point for each number card and three points for each bracket card used. Give each group a timer to add more pace to the game.
● You might consider some other optional rules to the activity, such as insisting that the bracket cards are always used, or increasing the score attached to them.
● Once the target number is made, work out the children's scores using your points system.

Plenary
● Write out the following missing number sentence on the board: __ (__ + __) + __ = 25. Challenge the children to find numbers that make the target number and complete the number sentence. Provide the numbers 2, 3, 4, 5 if the children are struggling.
● Challenge the children to find as many alternative solutions as possible.

Potential difficulties	Further support
Children may have difficulties recognising that 3(4+2) means multiply 3 by the sum of 4 and 2.	Discuss the idea of mathematical 'shorthand' with the children, and allow them to put the multiplication sign in until they are confident.

Moving on
● To make the game more demanding insist that the brackets should only be used when they are needed. For example, in 3 + 4 × 5, brackets are not needed unless the writer means (3 + 4) × 5 since we do multiplication before addition when calculating a number sentence with both of these operations.

Target cards

0	1	2	3	4
5	6	7	8	9
+	−	×	÷	(
+	−	×	÷	)

Logical numbers

Learning objectives
(Y4 and Y5) Solve mathematical problems or puzzles, recognise and explain patterns and relationships, generalise and predict.
(Y6) Recognise squares of numbers to at least 12 × 12.

Mental starter
See the starter 14 on page 14.

You will need
Photocopiable page 55 for each group; number cards 1 - 5 for each child.

Whole class work
● Write the following clues on the board:
My number is:
Greater than 20
Even
A multiple of 3.
● Ask: *What could my number be?* Discuss each solution and then gather the correct answers on the board – 24, 30, 36, 42 ...
● Add the following clue to the list – *My number is a multiple of 10.*
● Ask: *What happens to my list of possible answers now?* The list has been narrowed down to 30, 60, 90..., but many children may only want to consider 30. Point out that the other numbers fit all the clues and invite a final clue that will narrow the number down to 30.
● If there is time, repeat the activity with the following clues:
My number is:
Less than 20
A multiple of 5
A factor of 30
Even.

Individual work
● Give each child a copy of photocopiable page 55 and the number cards
1 - 5. (Reasoning activities are often best done individually and then explained to a partner, as discussion can interrupt or divert a train of thought.)
● The sets of clues are not designed to test understanding of number properties, but rather the use of these properties to solve reasoning problems. Encourage the children to explain the reasoning for their answers. Verbalising reasoning will help to give children confidence when solving multi-stage problems

Plenary
● Invite the children to share the puzzles they have made for themselves. It is quite possible that children will produce clues with no solution or with more than one – this is a demanding task and this way of working may be unfamiliar to children.

Moving on
● Publish the best sets of clues from the individual work and use them as regular puzzle exercises. The children will take pride when their work is being used and taken seriously by others and this will help to raise their self-esteem.
● Encourage the children to create further puzzles with the freedom to include other numbers or extend the nature of the clues. For example, they could include the properties of square numbers and allow clues such as *one more than a square number.*

Potential difficulties	Further support
Some children may have great difficulty with this sort of reasoning problem, especially if they are used to working on single-step problems.	Consolidate the ideas by offering more activities, such as those in the whole class activity above.

Name _____

Logical numbers

Use the number cards 1, 2, 3, 4, and 5 to help you find the solutions. Write your answers in the box.

Clues   **Answers**

1
There is an even number in the middle.
The 3 is immediately to the left of the 5.
The 4 is immediately to the right of the 1.
The numbers at each end add to 6.

1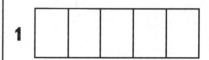

2
The odd numbers are all at one end.
The 5 is to the left of the 3.
The 4 has an odd number immediately to its left.
The 1 has an odd number either side.

2

3
The numbers at each end are both odd.
The 3 is not next to the 2 or the 4.
The 5 is next to the 2.
The 1 is not at the end.

3

4
The centre number is less than 3.
The last number is even.
The 4 is immediately to the right of the 5.
The first number is greater than 3.

4

5
The centre number is not 1.
The first number is not 5.
The 3 is not next to the 2.
The centre number is half of the last number.

5

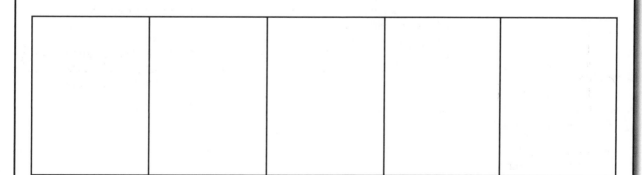

Make up one of your own for a partner to solve.
My clues.

Fraction groups

Learning objectives
(Y4) Use fraction notation.
Recognise simple fractions that are several parts of a whole, and mixed numbers.
(Y4) Find fractions of shapes.
(Y5) Recognise when two simple fractions are equivalent, including relating hundredths to tenths.

Mental starter
See the starter 15 on page 14.

You will need
Photocopiable page 57 for each child.

Whole class work
● Write the following seven fractions on the board: $\frac{1}{4}$, $\frac{1}{2}$, 0.25, 0.5, $\frac{4}{8}$, $\frac{3}{12}$, $\frac{4}{6}$.
● Say: *I want to put some of the fractions into a group – how can I do this?* (You may need to remind the children that decimals are just special fractions.)
● Ask the children for their reasoning when grouping fractions together. Some children may offer unusual groups such as, $\frac{1}{4}$, $\frac{4}{8}$ and $\frac{4}{6}$, as a group because they all have a 4 in them.
● Introduce the word 'equivalent' and explain that you want all of the fractions in a group to be the same size. Continue to question the children until you have two groups of equivalent fractions and one odd one. Ask: *Why does this fraction not fit into either group?*

Paired or small group work
● Ask each pair or small group to spread out a set of fraction cards (cut out from photocopiable page 57) face down.
● Ask the first player to pick a card and show it to the other players. If it is a 'word card' such as 'two-fifths' then they can begin collecting that equivalent set. They then have another go. If it is any other card it is returned face down to the table and play moves to the next player.
● The winner is the first player to collect all five cards from one set.
● Tell the children these additional rules:
  1) Players may collect from more than one set, but must start each set with the 'word card'.
  2) Whenever a player picks up a card from a set they are collecting they can have another go.

Plenary
● Return to the game introduced in the whole class work but include some simple equivalent percentages. Begin with sets that include 50% and 25%. Avoid sets that have thirds in them, as some children will have difficulty with 33 $\frac{1}{3}$ %, for example.

Potential difficulties	Further support
Fractions and the concepts surrounding them present many of the deep-seated misconceptions which prevail until adulthood.	It is important to use correct language and to explain equivalence using diagrams and models. Avoid explanations that offer only a procedural understanding such as: *To get an equivalent fraction, you do the same to the top and to the bottom.*

Moving on
● Invite the children to work as a group to try to put the entire set of fractions in order.
● If necessary, show the children how to compare fractions by comparing their decimal equivalents. They should not explicitly be told about common denominators at this stage.

Fraction groups

one half	$\frac{1}{2}$	0.5	$\frac{3}{6}$	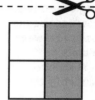
one quarter	$\frac{1}{4}$	0.25	$\frac{5}{20}$	
one fifth	$\frac{1}{5}$	0.2	$\frac{2}{10}$	
two fifths	$\frac{2}{5}$	0.4	$\frac{4}{10}$	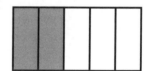
four fifths	$\frac{4}{5}$	0.8	$\frac{8}{10}$	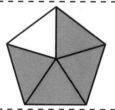
three quarters	$\frac{3}{4}$	0.75	$\frac{6}{8}$	
two thirds	$\frac{2}{3}$	0.666...	$\frac{4}{6}$	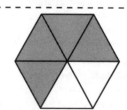

Measure for measure

Learning objectives
(Y4) Know and use the relationships between familiar units.
(Y5 and Y6) Use, read and write standard metric units.

Mental starter
See the starter 16 on page 15.

You will need
A copy of photocopiable page 59 for each pair or child; a metre stick; some of the objects listed on the activity sheet.

Whole class work

● Write on the board: *1km, 100m, 1000cm and 1000mm*. Ask the children to put these lengths in order. Advise them to take note of the units of each measurement. Use a metre stick and other resources to explain the lengths involved.
● Write on the board: *10kg, 100g, 10g, 1000g*. Repeat the procedure of the example above.
● Write on the board: *1km per hour and 10m per minute*. Ask the children to discuss these two speeds and to decide which is the faster. Ask them to explain their reasoning.

Individual or paired work

● Give each child a copy of photocopiable page 59. Ask the children to draw lines from each statement to the correct measurement. Encourage discussion about the reasonableness of their observations by making comparisons with familiar objects or speeds. There will always be variation in measurements taken in the real world. However, the measures have been selected so that only one is appropriate.

Plenary

● Discuss with the children how they decided on the answers to the questions on photocopiable page 59.
● It is important that children can support their estimates by referring to familiar objects and speeds. Have available some of the objects (or appropriate pictures) of things listed on the activity sheet.
● Continue with a discussion of the size of the world long jump record. This is currently 8m 95cm for men and 7m 52 cm for women. Set the distance up with masking tape on the classroom floor (or in a corridor if there is insufficient room). Children find these distances hard to believe. Up-to-date data of all athletics records can be accessed from the International Association of Athletics Federations (IAAF) website at www.iaaf.org/statistics/records,

Potential difficulties	Further support
Converting between units.	Have a conversion table available to allow children to remind themselves about conversion facts.
Children sometimes have very little experience of measuring 'in the real world'.	Give children opportunities to estimate measures, to discuss their estimations, and to check them against real measurements.

Moving on
● Give the children the following speeds and ask them to discuss them and then to put them in order: 20m per minute; 3km per hour; 100cm per second; 500mm per second.
● Discuss how it is important to convert them all into the same units first so that comparison is possible.

Measure for measure

◼ Draw a line from each statement to the approximate measurement.

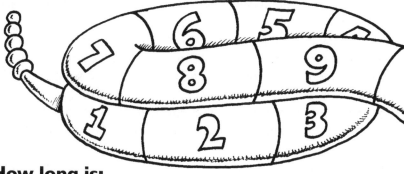

◼ **How long is:**

the length of a small car?	10m
the width of a thumb?	100m
the length of a bus?	2m
the diameter of a CD?	30cm
the length of a football pitch?	12cm
the height of a classroom door?	2cm
the length of a sheet of A4 paper?	4m

◼ **How heavy:**

is a new born baby?	5g
is an elephant?	1000g
is a small car?	2000g
is 1 litre of water?	3.5kg
is an egg?	5000kg
is a sheet of A4 paper?	1000kg
is a house brick?	50g

◼ **How fast:**

is an intercity train?	0.5mm per day
is a tortoise?	5m per minute
is the speed of light?	300 000km per second
is normal walking speed?	200m per hour
does your hair grow?	300m per second
does a cheetah run?	100km per hour
does sound travel?	6000m per hour

Measuring up

Learning objectives
(Y4) Use all four operations to solve word problems involving measures.
(Y5) Solve simple word problems involving numbers, based on measures, **explaining methods and reasoning.**
(Y6) Identify and use appropriate operations to solve word problems involving numbers and quantities, and explain methods and reasoning

Mental starter
See the starter 17 on page 15.

You will need
Photocopiable page 61 for each child; pencils; a 30cm piece of string; 30cm rulers; a 70cm piece of string or tape measure for each group.

Whole class work
- Give each child a short piece of string. Ask them to measure a pencil in centimetres and millimetres. Note if the children's answers are sensible.
- Now ask the children to use the string to measure a few of the objects on their tables. Alter the units so that sometimes you ask for the measurements in centimetres and millimetres and sometimes in millimetres alone.
- Invite the children to fold their string in half and to put a mark at the mid-point. Tell them to repeat this for each half of the string, and to mark the quarters.
- Say: *Measure carefully from one end to a quarter position and record this value in centimetres and millimetres.* Now ask them to double this value (preferably in their heads) and record the result. Ask: *What measurement will this give us?*
- Now ask them to double again. Finally, ask them to measure the whole length of the string and compare the results. Discuss differences between the two values and explain that any error in the first measurement has been doubled and doubled again.

Group work
- Give each child a copy of photocopiable page 61. This activity explores the accuracy of a method used by 'the Lilliputians' in *Gulliver's Travels* to calculate Gulliver's measurements. It requires the children to use string to measure around the thumbs of the children in their groups, and then to use this value to calculate wrist, neck and waist measurements.
- Ensure that the children make the first measurement around the thumb, as accurately as possible. If the children understand how to find average values, invite them to make several measurements and to enter the average.
- Support the children as they complete the sheet and discuss how useful and accurate they found the method to be.

Plenary
- Invite the children to relate their experiences using the rule. Discuss the use of the method and its merits and problems.

Potential difficulties	Further support
Children have difficulty measuring around a thumb accurately.	This measurement requires the use of fine motor skills and some children will need support. Suggest that the child being measured rests his or her hand on a table.

Moving on
- Ask the children to measure their arm spans (fingertips to fingertips) and heights. Try to decide which is larger. Use this opportunity to explore the use of a spreadsheet.
- Record the data in cm and use the graphing facility to draw a scatter graph for the children to interpret.

Measuring up

In the book *Gulliver's Travels*, by Jonathan Swift, Gulliver is a giant on the island of Lilliput. The Lilliputians need to make him a shirt but it is difficult to measure a giant. Instead they use a simple method to work out the size of his shirt and only need to measure around his thumb. Then they use this rule to work out the rest of the measurements:

Twice around the thumb is once around the wrist.
Twice around the wrist is once around the neck.
Twice around the neck is once around the waist.

■ You are going to investigate to see if this is true by measuring around a thumb and then doubling this value a few times.

■ **Here are the steps to take:**

1 Take a piece of string and measure around the thumb of a friend. You will need to measure as carefully and as accurately as you can.

2 Double this measurement and enter your answer value into the 'Wrist Calculated' column.

3 Measure your friend's wrist and enter this value.

4 Continue by calculating and measuring to get your friend's neck and waist values.

5 Do the same for three more people.

Name	Thumb		Wrist		Neck		Waist	
	Measured	Calculated	Measured	Calculated	Measured	Calculated	Measured	

■ Write about how useful and accurate this method is on the back of this sheet. Compare measured and calculated values.

Food for thought

Learning objectives
(Y4) Suggest suitable units and equipment to estimate or measure mass.
(Y4) Know and use the relationships between familiar units of mass.
(Y4) Know the equivalent of one half, one quarter, three quarters and one tenth of 1kg in grams.
(Y5 and Y6) Use, read and write standard metric units.
(Y5 and Y6) Convert larger to smaller units of mass and vice versa.
(Y5 and Y6) Suggest suitable units and measuring equipment to estimate or measure mass.

Mental starter
See the starter 18 on page 15.

You will need
Photocopiable page 63 for each child; packaged food items with the mass covered up (two different sized packets of breakfast cereals, a packet of biscuits, a small and large can of baked beans, a 1kg pack of potatoes, a 1kg and a ½kg bag of sugar, a packet of nuts, a chocolate bar, a box of tea bags, a bag of apples, a bag of crisps); a balance and a set of scales.

Moving on
● Invite the children to calculate the mass of a single tea bag based on the mass of the box. They should then weigh the item to check. This will need the use of sensitive scales.

Whole class work
● Write 1kg, ½kg, 0.1kg, 500g, ¼kg, 100g, 1000g randomly on the board.
● Say: *Give me two of these masses which are the same.* Continue until all three pairs have been identified.
● Ask: *Which mass is the odd one out?* Once ¼kg has been spotted, ask the children to convert it to grams.
● Hold up two items, one that is small but 'heavy' and the other, large but 'light'. Invite the children to 'weigh' the two items, one in each hand, and comment on which is heavier.
● Compare the two items using a balance, and then weigh them using scales. Explain that the balance compares two different weights and the scales measure a single mass (or weight) and offer a scale to read.

Group work
● Ask the children to begin by putting the selection of food packages in order of mass, using estimation and judgement. Make sure they cannot see the masses written on the packaging.
● Give each child a copy of photocopiable page 63. Explain that the children should record the name of each item, an estimate of its mass, and a measurement of its mass.
● Give the children two known masses with which to compare (for example, half a kilogram bag of sugar and a 50g bar of chocolate.
● Once all of the items have been estimated, ask the children to weigh and record the mass of each item, and discuss the accuracy of their estimates.
● Uncover the labels on the packaging and allow the children to complete the table. Ask them to check how accurate they were.
● Finally, ask them to calculate how much packaging each item has.

Plenary
● Invite the children to report back to the class. Focus on any surprises. Ask the children to comment on how much packaging there is.

Potential difficulties	Further support
Children have difficulty reading scales.	Go through reading the scales before the activity begins. Focus on any difficulties children may have interpreting unlabelled marks between numbers.

Food for thought

Item	Estimate of mass	What it weighs	What it says on the package	Mass of packaging							
Bag of sugar	1000g		1kg								

Decimal conversion

Learning objective
(Y5) Use decimal notation for tenths and hundredths.
(Y6) Use decimal notation for tenths and hundredths in calculations and when recording measurements.

Mental starter
See the starter 19 on page 16.

You will need
Photocopiable page 65 for each child; a metre stick graduated in mm.

Whole class work

● Take an example similar to that used on the activity sheet, in which there are two children of different heights. Write the height of one of them as 1.46m (give the person a name). Say that the other person is 20cm taller. Say: *Give me the height of the taller one in centimetres. What is their difference in height in metres?*

● Now say: *Their little sister is 60cm shorter than 1.46m. How tall is that?* Continue with another question like this, varying the use of centimetres and metres.

● Finally, check that the children can convert between pounds and pence and use the correct notation. Write on the board: *Cinema tickets £3.25.* Ask the children to convert this into pence. Ask: *How do I write this?*

● Next, ask the children to tell you how many pennies change you will get from £10.00. Invite the children to explain their working for this calculation.

Individual work

● Give each child a copy of photocopiable page 65. This is an individual activity but the children would benefit from discussing their ideas with each other.

● Remind the children of the units involved in converting length and check that all the children understand that, say, 0.43m is 43cm. During the activity, monitor children for correct notation and listen to their conversation to detect any misconceptions about the place-value nature of the activity.

Plenary

● Review the children's work and address any misconceptions. Use the table of prices from the activity. Ask target questions such as: *How much more expensive is the CD than the cake? What is that difference in pennies?*

● Follow up with: *How much change would I get from £10.00 if I bought all four items? How many pennies is that?*

Potential difficulties	Further support
Converting between whole numbers and hundredths, leaving out tenths.	It is important to use the correct language and to explain equivalence using diagrams and models. Avoid explanations that offer only a procedural understanding such as; *Just move the decimal point*.
Notation difficulties, such as children writing £2.54p or 1m.25cm.	With money calculations, remind the children that we use either pounds or pence but not both. With the second problem, children may not be aware that they are multiplying or dividing by 100.
If a calculator is used there may be notation difficulties when for example, £1.20 is seen as 1.2 on the display.	Practise interpreting results on a calculator display.

Moving on
● Ask the children to convert the heights of the children in the activity into mm. If possible, allow them to use a metre stick graduated in mm to help them.

Decimal conversion

◖ Complete this table.
Jack is 1.52m tall. He is 35cm taller than his younger sister, Amy. Their mum is 0.22m taller than Jack.

	Jack	Amy	Mum
Height m and cm			
Height in cm			

◖ Complete this table.
Amrita is 152cm tall. She is 28cm taller than her younger brother, Dinesh. Their dad is 43cm taller than Dinesh.

	Amrita	Dinesh	Dad
Height m and cm			
Height in cm			

◖ Complete this table.
The magazine is 88p. The CD is £3.99. The T-shirt is £1.50 more than the CD. The cake is 27p less than the magazine.

	Price in pounds & pence	Price in pence
CD		399p
Cake		
Magazine		
T-shirt		
All 4 items		

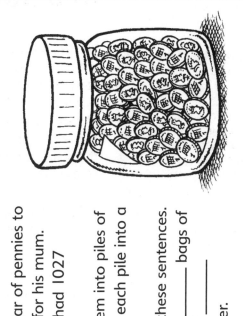

Steve saved a jar of pennies to buy a present for his mum. Altogether he had 1027 pennies.
He counted them into piles of £1.00 and put each pile into a bag.

◖ Complete these sentences.
Steve needed _____ bags of £1.00. He had _____ pennies left over.

In a spin

Whole class work

● Draw a horizontal line on the board. Mark on it the centre point and draw arrows to represent increasing and decreasing likelihood.
● Write the following five phrases on the board: *even chance, no chance, poor chance, good chance and certain.*
● Ask the children to place these terms on the line you have drawn at the point where they think they should be. Invite them to give you a sentence which uses the word in context and which justifies their choices.
● Ask: *What alternative words can I use for poor chance?* Proceed with the other terms until you are satisfied that the children have a good grasp of the language.

Paired or group work

● Give each pair or small group a copy of photocopiable page 67 and give each player a counter of a different colour. The game can be played by two to four players.
● The aim of the game is to navigate the course according to the outcome of the spinners. Players may choose which spinner to use in order to improve their chances of a favourable result.
● To use a spinner, place a paper clip in the centre of it and place your pencil at the centre of the spinner. Hold the pencil upright and now flick the paper clip to spin it. You move the number of spaces shown on the spinner. If the player lands on a hazard or reward square they must spin the spinner to determine their next move.
● To win, players must land exactly on the octagon shape at the end. There are a few hazards and rewards on the way and the choice of spinners will influence the players' chances of winning.

← —— **less likely**   **more likely** —— →

Plenary

● Discuss strategies for choosing one spinner over another. Ask: *Are the spinners fair?* This is a complex question, which is designed to encourage explanation rather than precision.

Potential difficulties	Further support
Children have difficulties with the basic concept of probability, and find it hard to understand that events have different outcomes according to chance.	Ask the children to look closely at the spinners and at the result they would like. Ask: *Which spinner offers the best chance of giving you the number you want?*

Name _____

In a spin

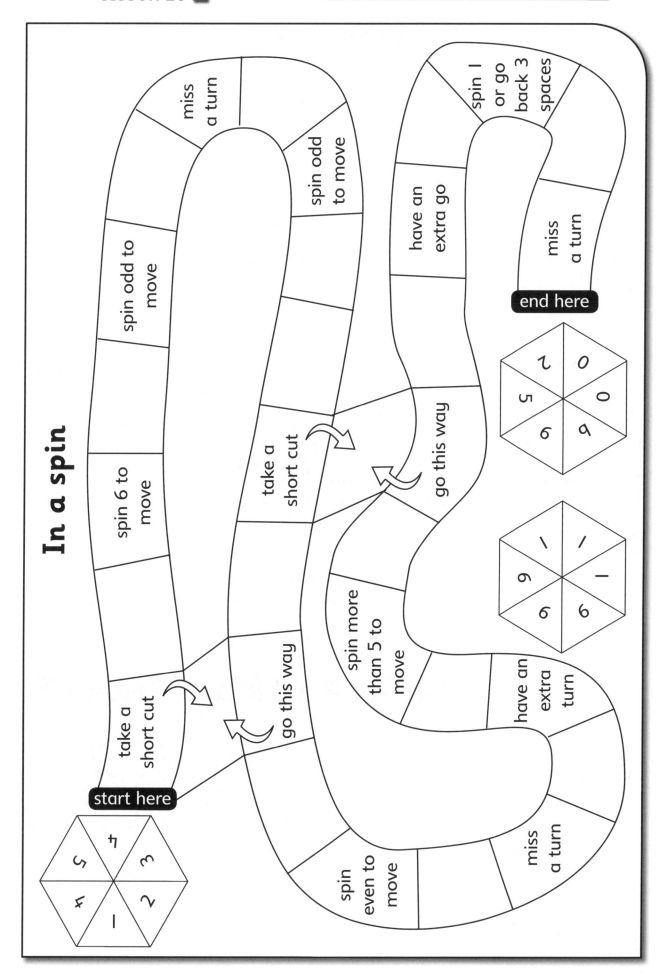

start here

end here

Reading scales

Learning objectives
(Y4 and Y5) Record estimates and readings from scales to a suitable degree of accuracy.
(Y6) Convert smaller to larger units and vice versa. Know imperial units.

Mental starter
See the starter 21 on page 16.

You will need
Photocopiable page 69 for each child; examples of items with scales to read such as kitchen scales, bathroom scales, thermometers, spring balances and so on; National Numeracy Strategy 'Interactive Teaching Program' for the starter ('Scales' activity).

Moving on
● Invite the children to use the scale in question 5 on photocopiable page 69 to convert two gallons into litres, then 14 litres into gallons. Tell them that these conversions are approximate.
● Ask them to use the scale in question 6 to convert 0° C to Fahrenheit and 40°F to Celsius.

Whole class work

● Before you begin there are two language issues to attend to with the whole class. First, make sure that the children recognise that the word 'scales' can refer to both the device used for measuring, and the drawing of the dial or line used to show a value. Use bathroom scales as an example. Second, make sure that the children understand the term 'units of measurement', and that they do not confuse the word 'units' with the use of the word in number work.

● Look at each of the items available in turn. Use the example items to illustrate scale, discussing each item's range and the units involved.

● Point to the bathroom scales. Ask: *What units of measurement are used?* (Some children will measure their body mass (weight) in stones and pounds, and they may not know the metric equivalent.) Repeat this with the other items available.

Individual work

● Give each child a copy of photocopiable page 69. For each picture, ask the children to first look at the scale, decide the units used and record the full name.

● Ask them to read the scale and to record its value, with the abbreviation for the units.

● Finally, ask them to write down an item that might be measured, using the measuring scales shown.

● Although this is an individual activity, the children will benefit from discussing the scales in pairs.

Plenary

● Use the activity sheet to ask a range of questions. For example, identify one scale and ask the children to tell you the largest value shown on the scale. Ask: *Can you show me where the mid-point of the scale is?*

● Try altering the units where appropriate. For example, ask for the ruler to be read in millimetres.

Potential difficulties	Further support
Difficulties in reading scales.	Practise reading the scales before the activity begins. Focus on any difficulties the children may have in interpreting unlabelled marks between numbers. Try using a spare copy of the activity sheet and indicate some additional marks for the children to read.

Reading scales

The units on this scale are _____
The arrow points to _____
I would use this scale to measure _____

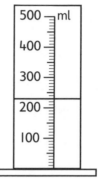

The units on this scale are _____
The level in the beaker is _____
I would use this scale to measure _____

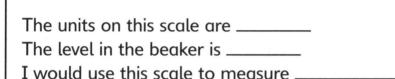

The units on this scale are _____
The arrow points to _____
I would use this scale to measure _____

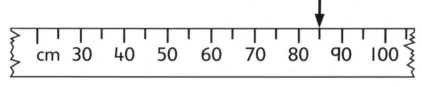

The units on this scale are _____
The arrow points to _____
I would use this scale to measure _____

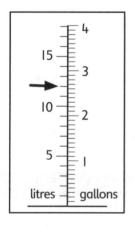

The units on this scale are _____
The arrow points to _____
I would use this scale to measure _____

This scale measures _____
It is _____°F
It is _____°C

Everything in proportion

Mental starter
See the starter 22 on page 17.

You will need
Photocopiable page 71 for each pair or child.

Whole class work
● Write the following recipe for oat flapjacks on the board. Show that this recipe makes ten flapjacks. Setting the data out in a table may help to clarify the process. Leave the right-hand column blank or add to it later.

For 10 flapjacks	For 20 flapjacks	For 5 flapjacks	
20g brown sugar			
100g butter			
40ml golden syrup			
180g oats			
1 teaspoon ground ginger			

● Say: *I want to make 20 flapjacks – how much sugar will I need?* Ask the children to explain their reasoning. Ask the children for the quantities of the other ingredients. Make sure that they are aware of the units involved.
● Then ask: *Suppose I only want to make five flapjacks instead of ten, how much sugar do I need?* Do the same for the other ingredients.

Individual or paired work
● Give each child a copy of photocopiable page 71. The activity is concerned with altering the ingredients of recipes in proportion. Make sure that the children are aware of the different units involved.
● Invite the children to work on the sheet individually then, when completed, pass their sheets to a partner for checking.
● Discuss with the children how they can alter a recipe for four into one for six. Try to identify a strategy that they can use independently.

Plenary
● Return to the recipe for flapjacks. Remind the children of the calculations they made earlier. Ask: *What would I do if I wanted a recipe for 30 flapjacks?*
● Discuss scaling up the recipe by multiplying each value in the first column by three.
● Now ask: *What about 25 flapjacks?* Help the children to realise that scaling can be combined with addition. They simply need to add together the ingredients for 20 and for 5.

Moving on
● Ask the children to use the final recipe on the activity sheet to produce a recipe for 18 muffins. This will involve them in a two-stage calculation, first halving and then addition.
● Note that although it is possible to do the calculations by multiplying by 1.5 it is likely to be too demanding for the children. Be aware that children may have difficulty understanding an expression such as 'half as much again'.

Potential difficulties	Further support
Some children alter measurements by addition or subtraction, rather than using proportion.	Have a scale model of a car (or similar) available to explain how each measurement is scaled by multiplication.

Everything in proportion

■ Change this biscuit recipe for 10 party biscuits into one for 30 biscuits.

Makes 10 large biscuits	Makes 30 large biscuits
60g unsalted butter	_____ g unsalted butter
40g golden syrup	_____ g golden syrup
45g caster sugar	_____ g caster sugar
50g ground almonds	_____ g ground almonds
30g plain flour	_____ g plain flour

■ Change this pancake recipe for four people into one for 8 people and one for 6 people. Include the units for each ingredient.

Pancake recipe for 4 people	Pancake recipe for 8 people	Pancake recipe for 6 people
120g plain flour	_____ plain flour	_____ plain flour
2 eggs	_____ eggs	_____ eggs
200ml milk	_____ milk	_____ milk
80ml water	_____ water	_____ water
50g butter	_____ butter	_____ butter

■ Change this recipe for 24 chocolate muffins into one for 12 muffins.

Chocolate muffin recipe (makes 24)	Chocolate muffin recipe (makes 12)
50g dark chocolate	_____ dark chocolate
150g plain flour	_____ plain flour
6 teaspoons cocoa powder	_____ teaspoons cocoa powder
2 teaspoons baking powder	_____ teaspoons baking powder
2 small eggs	_____ small eggs
40g sugar	_____ sugar
120ml milk	_____ milk

Calendars

Learning objectives
(Y4) Read simple timetables and use this year's calendar.
(Y5) Use all four operations to solve simple word problems involving numbers and quantities based on 'real life', **including time.**
(Y6) Explain methods and reasoning.

Mental starter
See the starter 23 on page 17.

You will need
Photocopiable page 73 for each child; copies of an old 'one month to a page' calendar; a computer calendar program; ruler.

Whole class work
● Show the children a large calendar showing the month just passed. Ask: *On what day of the week was the first day of the month?* and: *What was the date of the first Saturday in the month?*
● Ask similar questions until you are sure that all children are confident with reading a calendar. Consider conducting this activity on an interactive whiteboard using a computer-based calendar.
● Once the children can read or interpret the calendar, make sure that they understand the structure. Point out that the days increase by seven as you move down. Tell them that calendars may also show a few days of the previous month and next month.
● Using a ruler, cover up a row on the calendar. Point to a space covered by the ruler and ask: *How can I work out this date?* Continue with questions such as: *What day of the week is the...?*

Individual or paired work
● This is a demanding activity for less confident children, but with appropriate support they can succeed at it.
● Give each pair a page from an old calendar showing an entire month. Ask them to check the pattern of numbers. Ask: *How can you work out the numbers down and across the page if you are only given one date?*
● Give each child a copy of photocopiable page 73 and point out the initial pattern in the numbers. Ask them to check with you once they have completed the first calendar.
● Gather the whole group at this point for a 'mini plenary' to make sure that the concepts are secure.

Plenary
● Return to the calendars that the children have completed. Ask: *On what day of the week is/was 4th September in 2006?*
● On the calendar for the current month ask: *What is the date of the first/last day shown on the calendar?* Invite a child to explain how they worked out where the numbers went from today's date.

Potential difficulties	Further support
The children have difficulty placing 'today' on the calendar for this month.	Suggest they choose the column (the day) then work out how far through the month they are. For those really struggling, fill in 'today' for them.

Moving on
● If extra material is needed then give the children a fresh copy of photocopiable page 73 and ask them to create the calendar for next month using this month's calendar as a starting point.

Name _____

Calendars

■ Complete this calendar for the month of August 2006.

August 2006						
Sun	Mon	Tues	Wed	Thur	Fri	Sat
30 July	31 July	1	2			
		8				
				31	1 Sept	2 Sept

■ Check today's date, then complete the calendar for this month.

Sun	Mon	Tues	Wed	Thur	Fri	Sat

Stopping distances

Learning objectives
(Y4) Solve a problem by representing and interpreting data in bar charts - intervals labelled in 10s.
(Y5) Represent and interpret data in charts.
(Y6) Solve a problem by (representing), **extracting and interpreting information presented in charts.**

Mental starter
See the starter 24 on page 18.

You will need
Photocopiable page 75 for each child; coloured pencils a copy of *The Highway Code* (section 103, concerned with driving speeds). You can access a copy of the relevant page at www.highwaycode.gov.uk/09.htm

Moving on
● Tell the children that in some parts of Europe, drivers may drive at 80mph. Ask them to use the data to predict the stopping distance. Make sure that they calculate all three sections, the thinking distance, the braking distance and the total stopping distance.

Whole class work
● Offer some preliminary work, to remind the children about the different types of road and different types of vehicle.
● Refer to the section of *The Highway Code* that illustrates driving speeds. Ask questions such as: *What is the maximum allowed speed for a car towing a caravan on a single carriageway?* and: *Why is this slower than for a car alone?*
● Continue with other questions that relate to the chart. Refer to the section that shows the stopping distances for cars under normal conditions.

Individual or paired work
Give each child a copy of photocopiable page 75 Explain that the data shows the distance it takes to stop under normal driving conditions. Explain the terms, 'thinking distance' and 'braking distance'. Since these two items are really referring to times, the children need to understand and be able to interpret this unusual use of the terms.
● Ask the children to complete the missing items in the table.
● Now help the children to complete the second part of the activity. Explain that each bar in the bar graph must be made of two parts, just like the example shown. Encourage the children to colour or shade the thinking and braking distances in different colours. Make sure they do not colour the bars arbitrarily.

Plenary
● Try to give the children a feel for how far the stopping distances are. For example, explain that at 70mph the stopping distance of 96 metres is the length of a sports pitch.
● Ask the children if they think the stopping distances will be the same in wet conditions. Ask: *Why will the distances increase?*

Potential difficulties	Further support
Some children may have difficulty in interpreting a bar graph in which two bars are joined.	Explain that the bars are joined because the total stopping distance is made up of two parts - the thinking distance and the braking distance.

Stopping distances

◾ Complete this table of the stopping distances for a car driving in dry, normal conditions.

Speed in mph	Thinking distance in metres	Braking distance in metres	Total stopping distance in metres
10			
20	6	6	
30	9	14	
40	12	24	36
50	15	38	
60	18		73
70		75	96

The Highway Code does not include a stopping distance for 10mph. Use the data in the table to estimate a value for both the thinking distance and the braking distance.

◾ Complete the data for the total stopping distances.

◾ Use the grid below to make a bar graph showing this data. Shade the thinking distance first and then extend the bar by adding the braking distance.

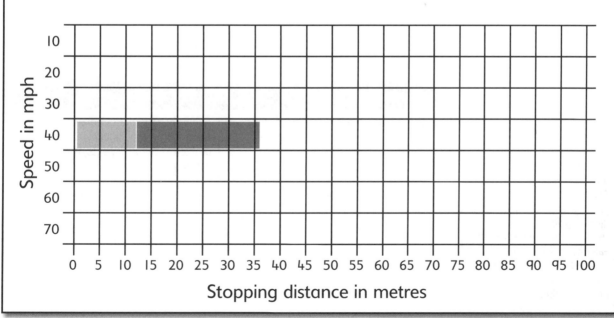

Tricky grids

Whole class work

● Draw the section shown right of a multiplication grid on the board:

● Explain to the children that this is part of a multiplication grid, but that some numbers are missing. Say that the numbers along the edges are also not in the right order.

×	5		
	35		
4			24
9		72	

● Ask the children to identify the easiest cells to fill in, such as those that need direct multiplication. Point to one of these cells – such as that containing the product of 9 and 5, and ask for the answer.

● Move on to the cells that require a division calculation. Ask: *What calculation do I perform to get the answer in this cell?* Continue until all of the cells are complete.

● Some of the entries are directly available on the grid – for those that are more difficult, tell the children to look for the numbers in the grid on their multiplication tables. If the children are struggling, then give them a multiplication grid. They will still have a lot of work to do, since the tables on 'Tricky grids' are not in the right order.

Individual work

● Give each child a copy of photocopiable page 77. Explain that they should look for the easiest calculation first and that they can work their way around each grid in any order.

● The final grid is more demanding and the children will need to spot the few starting points and work their way around logically.

Plenary

● Invite the children to explain how they worked out the final grid. Ask: *Which was the first number you found?* Encourage them to offer an explanation and reason for each step. If the children need prompting, then ask them how they can use the 40 to find out one of the tables. Also, ask them if they know where the number 99 appears on a multiplication grid.

● If possible, share a grid created by one of the children from the 'Moving on' activity below.

Potential difficulties	Further support
The children are insecure with their tables.	Allow the use of a calculator so that the children can concentrate on the problem-solving aspects of the activity.

Name _____

Tricky grids

■ Complete these multiplication grids.

×	7	6	
3	21		
5			20
8			

×	6	7	
8			
		21	
		35	45

×	7	6	
7			
6			30
			55

×			7
7	21		
	18		42
		72	56

×	7	8			5
				36	
				72	40
7					
				54	
	63	99			

Three-cornered search

Learning objectives
(Y4) Describe and visualise 3-D and 2-D shapes. Recognise equilateral and isosceles triangles.
(Y4) Classify polygons using criteria such as number of right angles, whether or not they are regular, symmetry properties.
(Y5) Classify triangles (isosceles, equilateral, scalene), using criteria such as lines of symmetry.

Mental starter
See the starter 26 on page 18.

You will need
Photocopiable page 79 for each child; pin boards.

Whole class work
Make sure that the children understand the different properties of triangles. Draw four different triangles on the board: isosceles, scalene, right-angled and equilateral. Write the four properties on the board (but not adjacent to their respective triangles). Remind the children about the properties and their definitions.

● Say: *Help me to match the properties to the triangles.* Point to a triangle and ask: *Which property goes with this triangle?* When correctly identified, draw a line from the triangle to the property. Repeat for the other triangles.
● Note that the right-angled triangle will also be either isosceles or scalene. Point this out to the children and ask them to decide which it is. Draw the other version to illustrate.
● Draw more examples of each triangle until the children are secure in their understanding.

Individual work
● Give each child a copy of photocopiable page 79. Explain the use of dotted paper to draw triangles.
● Each triangle the children draw must be different. Take a few moments to explain that 'different' means that we cannot turn one triangle into another by reflecting it or rotating it.
● Give each child a pin board (where available) to model the triangles and compare them. Remind the children that they should only be working on 3 × 3 pin board grids. Tell the children that there are eight different triangles to find.
● As the children complete the table at the bottom of the activity sheet it is important to help them to realise that some triangles have more than one property.

Plenary
● The children will have given different letters to different triangles, making discussion around the class difficult. Therefore, draw a grid and a triangle on the board and ask the children which categories it falls into.
● To help the children know if a triangle is equilateral or not, describe the lengths of each side in terms of a journey from one corner to the next. Encourage the children to see that one side is different from the other two in the examples.

Moving on
● All isosceles triangles have a line of symmetry. Invite the children to draw the lines of symmetry on their triangles.
● The children may discover that one way to define a scalene triangle is one with no lines of symmetry.

Potential difficulties	Further support
Children will have difficulty believing that none of the triangles are equilateral.	Demonstrate that sides that appear to be the same are, in fact, different in length. The property of 'equilateral' has been included in the table for completeness.

Three-cornered search

■ Join some dots to make a *different* triangle in each grid.

A

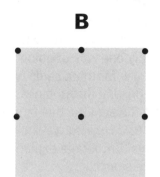

B

C

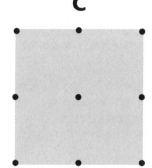

D

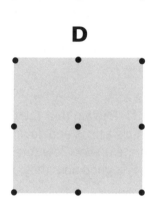

E

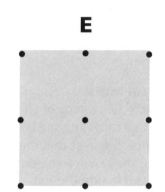

F

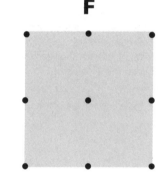

G

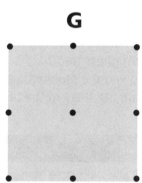

H

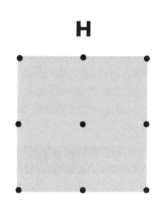

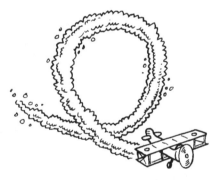

■ Record the properties of each triangle by ticking some boxes. Some triangles have more than one property. Your teacher might ask you to justify your choice of property.

	A	B	C	D	E	F	G	H
Equilateral								
Isosceles								
Right-angled								
Scalene								

Magic crosses

Learning objectives
(Y4, Y5 and Y6) Solve mathematical problems or puzzles, recognise and explain patterns and relationships, generalise and predict.

Mental starter
See the starter 27 on page 19.

You will need
Photocopiable page 81 and 1 – 9 number cards for each child (include zero for each child in the 'Moving on' activity).

Whole class work

- Give each child a set of 1 - 9 number cards. Ask them to hold up three cards with a total of ten. Comment on the variety of ways of doing this.
- Now ask for three cards with a total of six. Comment on the fact that there is only one way of doing this.
- Finally, ask for three cards with a total of five. Invite the children to comment on why this is impossible.
- Repeat the activity, this time asking for a total of 15 with three odd numbers. Ask: *How do we know that we have found all of the ways of solving this?* Encourage explanations that show an understanding of an exhaustive search.
- Ask: *What about three numbers that total 12? Can it be done with three odd numbers?* Invite the children to reason why this is impossible. Encourage them to explain based on the fact that the sum of two odd numbers is always even, and that a third odd number will make the total odd again.

Individual work

- Give each child a copy of photocopiable page 81. Explain that they must put five cards into the boxes so that the totals across and down are the same. Suggest that the children concentrate on very low totals first. When they have a solution, that they think is a good one, they should record it on the sheet.

Plenary

- Discuss the children's solutions and decide upon the lowest and highest possible totals. (Check that no solution uses duplicate numbers.) Ask: *How can we be sure that this is the lowest/highest total?*
- Encourage the children to explain how they solved the problem, such as first selecting appropriate cards and then arranging them in the best possible way.

Potential difficulties	Further support
Children may have difficulty working systematically, and be unable to notice a duplicate solution or one that is missing.	Suggest that low totals come from using low-value cards and that the children should try 1, 2, 3, 4 and 5 first.

Moving on
- Challenge the children to arrange five numbers in the cells on the activity sheet so that the number in the centre is the sum of those either side and also the sum of those above and below. One possible solution has 8 in the middle, with 6 and 2 on the sides, and 1 and 7 above and below. Ask the children to record all of the possible solutions they can find.
- Invite children to explore magic crosses that include zero.

Magic crosses

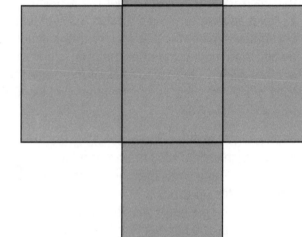

■ Record magic crosses with low magic totals. Put a loop around the one with the lowest total.

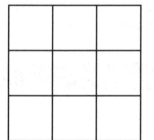  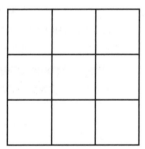 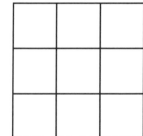

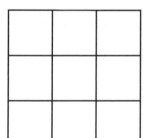 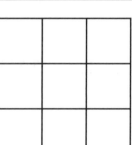 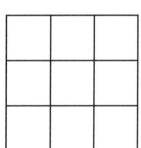 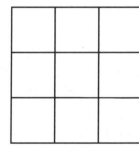

■ Record magic crosses with high magic totals. Put a loop around the one with the highest total.

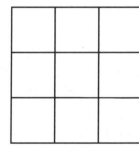

Magic squares

Learning objectives
(Y4, Y5 and Y6) Solve mathematical problems or puzzles, recognise and explain patterns and relationships, generalise and predict.
(Y4) Recognise odd and even numbers up to 1000, and some of their properties.
(Y5 and Y6) Make general statements about odd or even numbers.

Mental starter
See the starter 28 on page 19.

You will need
Photocopiable page 83 and 1 - 9 number cards for each child (plus zero cards for the 'Moving on' activity).

Whole class work
● Give each child a set of 1 - 9 number cards. Say: *Hold up three cards with a total of 15.* Discuss some of the children's solutions, then ask each child to change two of their cards and make 15 another way.
● Next, ask the children to change two of their cards again but keep a total of 15 (some children may find this difficult).
● Continue with: *Can anyone make 15 with just odd numbers?* There are two ways to do this - with either the 3, 5 and 7, or with the 1, 5 and 9.
● Ask if anyone can find a total of 15 with just even numbers. Encourage explanations as to why this is impossible (when even numbers are added together the total is always even).
● Make a list on the board of all of the combinations that make 15. Make the list accessible for the individual work if the children have found this stage difficult.

Individual work
● Give each child a copy of photocopiable page 83. Explain that they must put all nine cards into the boxes so that every row, column and diagonal adds up to 15.
● Discuss the different possible ways of making 15. Draw attention to that fact that the number 5 is involved in many of them.
● If necessary suggest that the children put 5 in the middle.
● Ask the children to record their solutions on the activity sheet. The aim is to find as many different ones as possible. Explain that they can find new solutions from old ones by swapping the numbers around.

Plenary
● Discuss the children's solutions. Ask them to describe the symmetry they have found. Ask the children how we can turn one solution into another. (All eight of the possible solutions are related by reflection and rotation of a single magic square.)

Potential difficulties	Further support
The children may have difficulty making rows, columns and diagonals make 15 at the same time.	Introduce the idea of an 'almost magic square', in which some of the lines add to 15, but not all of them. If they find one they should record and write 'almost magic' under the solution. Usually, these squares can be turned into magic squares by interchanging pairs of numbers.

Moving on
● Give the children a fresh copy of the activity sheet and ask them to explore magic squares that include zero in place of nine. They will need to find the magic total for this set of numbers. If they are unable to do this then tell them that it is 12. As with the individual activity there are eight solutions.

Magic squares

◼ Record your magic squares here. Make sure each one has the same total in each row, column and diagonal.

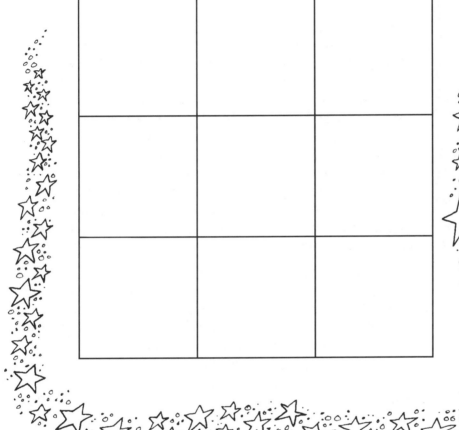
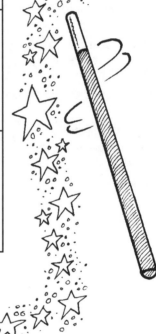
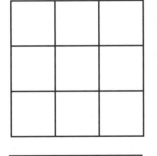
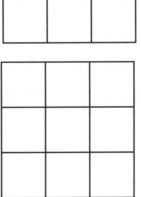
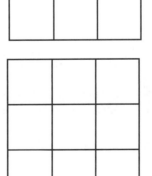
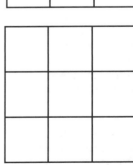

Divide it up

Learning objectives
(Y4) Begin to relate fractions to division.
(Y4) Use fraction notation.
Recognise the equivalence of simple fractions.
(Y5) Relate fractions to division.
(Y6) Use a fraction as an operator to find fractions of numbers or quantities.

Mental starter
See the starter 29 on page 20.

You will need
Photocopiable page 85 for each child.

Moving on
● Invite the children to create one of these problems of their own. Suggest that the main number involved has lots of factors so that there are plenty of options for the fractions.

Whole class work

● Draw a bar of chocolate on the board as a 6 × 4 array of squares. Ask: *How many square of chocolate are there? If I eat one-third of them, how many squares is that?* Continue with similar fractions, such as one-quarter and one eighth.

● Ask: *How many squares is two-thirds of the bar?* If the children have difficulty, draw another bar the same size and shade in two-thirds of it. When discussing the problem, refer the children to their answer for one third of the bar, found earlier.

● Continue with: *If I eat four squares what fraction is that?* If the children answer $\frac{4}{24}$, then discuss equivalent fractions. Finally, ask: *What fraction remains after I have eaten four squares?*

● Make an accurate number line with zero at one end of the line and 24 at the other. Return to the questions above, but mark one-third with a loop from zero to eight. An advantage of the number line model can be seen when you ask for two-thirds. This becomes a 'journey' of two 'loops', each of which is one-third. Many children find using number lines easier as they find it easier to visualise length rather than area.

Individual work

● Give each child a copy of photocopiable page 85. Explain that the activity involves understanding the word problem first. Suggest that to start with they record fractions in the form suggested by the story, before they are reduced to their lowest terms.

● Provide cubes or counters for questions 2, 3 and 4, to emphasise the sharing aspect of working with fractions. Some children may be happy with a number line, but it must be accurate. In the case of £5.00 the number line needs to be from 0 to 500, not 0 to 5, with inches and tenths offering a useful scale. The children will be cutting and sharing the whole line – quite a demanding concept.

Plenary

● Fractions are often represented as parts of a 'pie'. Draw a circle on the board and use it to illustrate how the fractions in the final question can be represented in this form. The twenty-fourths can all be represented as twelfths.

● To divide a circle into twelfths, first divide it into quarters and then divide the quarters into thirds.

● For some children this plenary might be too demanding. If this is the case, return to the diagram used in the main activity but use it to solve the final question.

Potential difficulties	Further support
Many children find both word problems and fractions difficult.	Concentrate on solving the problem in words first. Invite the children to make jottings of intermediate answers. Encourage the children to set the problem out with cubes or counters.

Divide it up

◀ Read each of the sentences and then join the lines to the correct fractions.

Sandeep gets £5.00 a week pocket money. He spends half of it on a present for his mum, one quarter on sweets and the rest he saves.

£1.25	£2.50	£1.25

present	sweets	save

There are 30 children in Tom's class. They filled in a survey about how they travelled to school. Six children came by car, ten of them came by bus, five came by bicycle and the remainder walked.

$\frac{1}{3}$	$\frac{1}{5}$	$\frac{1}{6}$	$\frac{3}{10}$

car	bicycle	walk	bus

Suki asked 20 people which team they support. Five only support 'United', four only support 'City', three only support 'Rovers' and eight support all three.

$\frac{3}{20}$	$\frac{1}{5}$	$\frac{1}{4}$	$\frac{2}{5}$

City	United	all three teams	Rovers

$\frac{1}{3}$	$\frac{5}{12}$	$\frac{1}{6}$	$\frac{1}{12}$

Jane is at school for 8 hours, sleeps for 10 and watches TV for 2 hours.

sleep	watch TV	at school	rest of the day

Make 1001

Learning objectives
(Y4) Estimate and check by approximating. Check with an equivalent calculation.
(Y5) Check with the inverse operation when using a calculator. Estimate by approximating, then check result.
(Y5 and Y6) Develop calculator skills and use a calculator effectively.

Mental starter
See the starter 30 on page 20.

You will need
Photocopiable page 87 and a calculator for each child.

Whole class work
● Write the following numbers on the board 12, 24, 33, 40, 45, 56, 61, 77, 68, 89, 91.
● Tell the children that some of these numbers can be paired with a partner to make 101 and that one of the numbers has no partner.
● Ask the children to find two numbers which add to 101. When a pair is offered, ask: *How did you work that out? Can you find another pair?*
● When five different pairs are found, ask the children to identify the number without a pair. Ask: *Can you find three numbers which add to 101?*

Individual work
● Give each child a copy of photocopiable page 87 and a calculator. Discuss some strategies for finding pairs of numbers that add to 1001. For example, one of them must be odd and the other even. Suggest that if they are starting with a low number then it is sensible to try higher numbers for its partner.
● Encourage the children to use mental strategies to approximate and narrow down the options to one or two numbers, before using the calculator. The calculator should not be used as a checking device in which children simply go through the list and check every number.
● Suggest that the children put a loop around numbers once they have been used. They should not cross them out as this will make the second part of the activity more difficult.

Plenary
● Use the numbers on the activity sheet to remind the children about the concept of difference.
● Ask the children for two numbers with a difference of 444. Challenge them to find the pair of numbers with the largest difference. Ask: *How do you know this pair of numbers has the largest difference?*
● Continue by asking for the pair of numbers with the smallest difference, a difference between 100 and 200, a difference that is odd and so on.

Potential difficulties	Further support
Children may have difficulty with the place-value concepts required in order to use mental strategies as part of the activity.	Have place-value cards available to remind children of the value of each of the digits. Alternatively, a metre stick graduated in mm provides a good number line model. The number line will help children to gain a clear understanding of the size of the numbers involved.

Moving on
● There is one set of three numbers on the activity sheet which adds to make 2001. Can the children discover this set of numbers? Add this set to the bottom of the activity sheet. The numbers are 900, 720 and 381.

Make 1001

234	767	767
900	381	480
521	99	789
620	902	111
137	864	101
281	720	890

1) Find and record pairs of numbers which add to 1001.

_____ + _____ = 1001   _____ + _____ = 1001   _____ + _____ = 1001

_____ + _____ = 1001   _____ + _____ = 1001   _____ + _____ = 1001

2) Can you find two sets of three numbers which add to 1001? One number in each set has been found for you.

381 + _____ + _____ = 1001   _____ + _____ + 720 = 1001

Ratio

Learning objectives
(Y4) Begin to use ideas of simple proportion.
(Y5) Solve simple problems using ideas of ratio and proportion.
(Y6) Solve simple problems involving ratio and proportion.

Mental starter
See the starter 31 on page 20.

You will need
Photocopiable page 89 for each child.

Whole class work

- Draw a row of boxes on the board. Say that you want to shade one box in every three. Ask: *How can I do this?*
- Invite a child to shade some boxes and observe the strategy used. Repeat with another row of boxes, saying that you want to shade in three in every four boxes.
- Draw a bag of sweets on the board and write 12 on it to represent the number of sweets. Explain that there are only strawberry and raspberry sweets in the bag and that there are two strawberry sweets for each raspberry sweet.
- Ask: *How many of each flavour of sweet are there?* Continue with: *How did you work it out?* Change the number of sweets in the bag to 24 and repeat the questions.
- Support the children in identifying that by doubling the number of sweets you will also double the number of each flavour. Explain that there are still two strawberry sweets for each raspberry sweet, and that there are eight raspberry sweets. Draw a picture to help if necessary. Ask: *How many strawberry sweets are there? How many altogether?*
- Finally, say that another bag has 12 strawberry sweets. Ask: *How many sweets altogether?* Make sure that the children can use and understand the relationship in this inverse way.

Individual work

- Give each child a copy of photocopiable page 89. Work closely to support the children as they may struggle to relate this work to practical examples that are familiar to them.

Plenary

- Revise the final question on the activity sheet and ask the children for their strategies.
- Alter the question by saying that another club has 24 members, with equal numbers of boys and girls. This time, six boys join the club. Ask: *How many boys are there now?* Ask the children to complete the statement: *There are ___ girls for every ___ boys.*

Potential difficulties	Further support
Children may interpret the words in the first part of the activity in a different way. For example, when asked to shade two in every three, they may shade two and then leave three and so on.	Concentrate on helping the children to understand the language. For example, to understand '2 in every 3', show the children how to take the second item (the 3) first and then refer back to the 2.

Moving on
- Give the children a piece of squared paper and ask them to produce shaded patterns to match the following statements:
    Shade 3 in every 5
    Shade 3 in every 8
    Shade 2 in every 7.
- If the children find this straightforward ask them to draw each pattern in a rectangular array.

Ratio

Shade 1 tile in every 3.

Shade 2 tiles in every 5.

Shade 2 tiles in every 3.

Shade 3 tiles in every 5.

ORANGE AND LEMON CRINKLES

INSIDE EACH BAG THERE ARE 2 ORANGE CRINKLES FOR EACH LEMON CRINKLE!

This bag has 10 orange Crinkles. The bag has

_____ lemon Crinkles and

_____ sweets altogether.

Here is a bag of Crinkles.

It has _____ orange Crinkles

and _____ lemon Crinkles.

These 5 bags of Crinkles are all the same size. There are 30 sweets altogether.

In each bag there are

_____ orange Crinkles

and _____ lemon ones.

The school sports club has two girls for every boy. There are 36 children in the club. There are _____ boys and _____ girls in the club. After a number of boys join the club the numbers are equal. This means that _____ boys joined the club.

The school music club has 24 members, with an equal number of boys and girls. six boys leave the club. There are now _____ boys and _____ girls in the club.

Around the pitch

Learning objectives
(Y4) Measure and calculate the perimeter of rectangles.
(Y5) Understand, measure and calculate perimeters of rectangles.
(Y6) Calculate the perimeter of simple compound shapes that can be split into rectangles.

Mental starter
See the starter 32 on page 21.

You will need
Photocopiable page 91 for each child; squared paper (for 'Further support' and 'Moving on').

Whole class work
● Draw a rectangle on the board and label its length as 50m and its width as 30m. Say: *At a school event, this boundary rope in the shape of a rectangle was set up. How long is the rope?*
● Give the children a while to work out the answer, then ask them to explain their reasoning. If the children identify a 'short cut', make sure that they understand where it comes from.
● Repeat with different dimensions such as: 60m by 40m, 55m by 30m and 65m by 35m. Explain that the rope goes around the edge of a rectangle and measures its perimeter.

Individual work
● Give each child a copy of photocopiable page 91. Explain that calculating the length of the white tape used on the all-weather pitch is just like calculating the length of rope needed. They are both perimeters of a rectangle.
● Some of the questions require additional reasoning. Encourage the children to see the problems in a practical way, and imagine walking around the edge with tape.

Plenary
● If the children feel confident it is useful for all of them to see you explain the 'Moving on' problem below. Tackle the problem in a practical way, making sure that all dimensions are marked on before working out the perimeter. Talk about each stage of the calculation.
● The children may need reminding that they have to add the boundary figure on twice to get the length and width measurements (once at each end). Make sure you explain this problem to the children.

Potential difficulties	Further support
Some children will have difficulty with the diagrams and their lack of detail.	Give children squared paper and show them how to draw a rectangle to scale. All of the rectangles in the activity can be drawn with a scale of 1cm to 10m. They can then 'count' around the edge.

Moving on
● Tell the children that Rosie has to mark out the pitch (60m by 30m) and a boundary for spectators (see right). The boundary is always 10m from the edge of the pitch. Ask the children to help her by working out how much tape is needed for the boundary of the pitch. Provide squared paper to help the children to set out the problem.
● Mark the dimensions when you have worked them out.

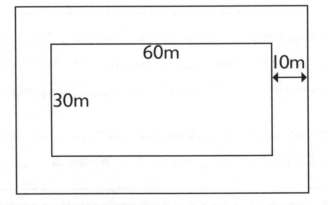

Around the pitch

- Rosie has been asked to use special white tape to mark out lines around the all-weather pitches. Look at the dimensions of each pitch and work out how much tape is needed.

70m

30m

This pitch needs _____ m of tape.

80m

35m

This pitch needs _____ m of tape.

85m

40m

This pitch needs _____ m of tape.

- She knows that this pitch is twice as long as it is wide.

80m

This pitch needs _____ m of tape.

- On this pitch she must mark the centre line as well.

80m

50m

This pitch needs _____ m of tape.

- Rosie decides to make two tables to help her with her calculations. Complete the tables for her.

Length of pitch in metres	Width of pitch in metres	Centre line in metres	Total length of tape
40	20	20	
50	25		
60	30		
70	40		

Length of pitch in metres	Width of pitch in metres	Total length of tape
50	20	
60	40	
50	30	
65	35	

50 MATHS LESSONS · AGES 9-11

Net me a cube

Learning objectives
(Y4) Make shapes and discuss properties.
(Y5 and Y6) Make shapes with increasing accuracy. Visualise 3-D shapes from 2-D drawings and identify different nets .

Mental starter
See the starter 33 on page 21.

You will need
Photocopiable page 93 for each pair; six Polydron squares or similar; squared paper.

Whole class work
● Draw a net of an open cube on the board (such as one that forms a cross). Ask: *How can we tell that this net will fold to make an open cube?* Invite the children to describe folding the sides.
● Now draw an incorrect net for an open-topped cube and ask: *How can we tell that this one will not fold to make an open cube?* Encourage the children to see that two of the sides overlap. Demonstrate with the linking squares.
● Ask the children to use the squared paper to draw all of the nets they can for an open cube. You may wish to give them linking squares for support, though the children should be encouraged to visualise the folding process. Collect the solutions on the board. (See page 105 of the *Framework for Teaching Mathematics* (DfEE) for examples.)
● The children may have difficulty deciding if two apparently different nets are the same or not. Discuss with the children what 'different' and 'the same' mean with respect to nets.

Paired work
● Give each child, in pairs, a copy of photocopiable page 93 and six linking squares. Ask them to arrange the six squares into the net of a cube and to check by folding them up. Ask the children to find the net they have made on the sheet and put a tick by it. (It is possible, but unlikely, that a child makes the net that is missing and which forms the final part of the activity.)
● Explain that the children need to find the 'impostors' in the list of nets. To do this they either make each one to check, or decide by folding the sides up mentally. The children should mark each net with a tick and those that are not nets with a cross. (The 'impostors' are C, F, L and N.) The missing net is shown here.

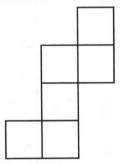

Moving on
● Ask the children to write a B in one square to represent the bottom of each cube. They must then put a T in the square that will be the top of each cube.

Plenary
● Collect together the suggested missing nets. Ask the children to test each one to see if it is correct.

Potential difficulties	Further support
Some children with poor motor skills may need to practise linking and unlinking squares.	Give the children some linking squares to experiment with before the lesson.

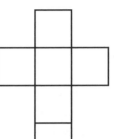

Net me a cube

■ There are 11 nets of a cube altogether. Hidden on this page are 10 of the nets and 4 impostors. Can you spot the nets?

A

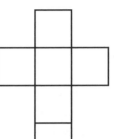

B

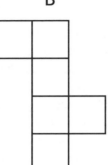

C

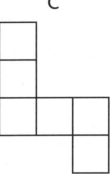

D

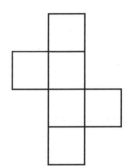

E

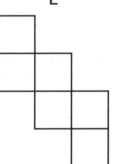

F

G

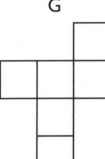

H

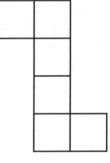

I

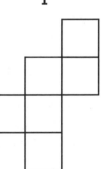

J

K

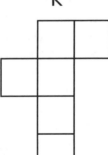

L

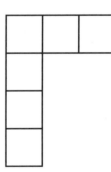

M

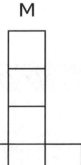

N

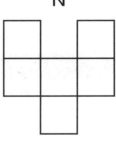

■ Find the missing net and draw it on the grid.

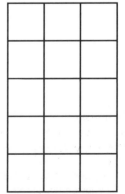

Missing numbers

Learning objectives
(Y4) Partition numbers into hundreds, tens and ones.
(Y5) Explain methods and reasoning, orally and in writing.
(Y6) Understand and use the relationships between the four operations.

Mental starter
See the starter 34 on page 22.

You will need
Photocopiable page 95 for each child; digit and symbol cards.

Whole class work

● Write the following in columns on the board: _34 + 5_4=79_. Ask the children to find which numbers are missing (the correct calculation is 234 + 564 = 798).
● When the solution is found, ask: *How did you work that out?* Encourage the children to use the inverse operation.
● Now try the more demanding calculation, 637 + 254 = 891 but leave out the 4, 6 and 9. If the children have difficulty, ask them to formulate a question that you will answer, to help them.
● Finally, write the calculation 6 × __ + 10 = 40 on the board. Ask the children to discuss in pairs how they would go about solving this. Focus on the children's methods and not the answers. Make sure that the children can use inverse operations and do not solve this simply by trial and improvement.

Individual work

● Give each child a copy of photocopiable page 95. Point out that the first three calculations use addition and the next three subtraction. Watch for misconceptions, such as assuming that addition calculations always involve only addition to solve them. Ask the children to check their answers by trying the calculation in full.
● To support a kinaesthetic approach during the second part of the activity, give the children digit and symbol cards so that they can lay out calculations and move the numbers around until they are satisfied with their answers.

Plenary

● Make up a set of large number cards with the numbers 2, 3, 4 and 5, and the symbols ×, + and –. Give each symbol to a different child and invite them to stand in front of the class. Say that they need to use all the numbers and symbols to make a number sentence with the largest possible answer.
● Take suggestions from the children and ask those holding the cards to rearrange themselves so that they can check the calculation. Ask the children to support their suggestions with reasons. Now ask: *How do we find the lowest possible answer?*
● An important discussion point is the order of operations. For example, if you do the calculation 2 + 3 × 4 you will get 20 on a four-function calculator, but 14 on a scientific calculator.

Potential difficulties	Further support
Some children may struggle with calculations that require the inverse operation.	Encourage children to see the calculation 2+_ =6 as *What must I add to 2 to make 6?* Many children focus only on the operation sign and may therefore offer 8 as the answer.

Moving on
● Ask the children to make up some missing numbers of their own, in which three digits are missing (as in the examples on the sheet).

Name _____

Missing numbers

■ Find the missing numbers in these calculations.

```
  H T U              H T U              H T U
    2 3                  3 6                  3 6
+ I   5            +  2 5             +  2 5
-------            -------            -------
  I 6                3   7              7   2
```

```
  H T U              H T U              H T U
  4   6              5 6                    6 2
- 2 5              - 2   3            -  2
-------            -------            -------
    3 2                2 4              2 2 8
```

5	× _____	+	4	=	I9
I2	+ _____	−	I4	=	I8
49	÷ _____	+ _____		=	I6

3	× _____	+	q	=	30
I2	× _____	+	I4	=	50
_____	÷	8	− 6	=	0

■ Find the missing symbols.

I5 _____ 3 _____ 25 = 70   I0 _____ 5 _____ I7 = 33

8 _____ 8 _____ 8 = 8 _____ q

■ Use only the numbers I, 2, 3, 4, 5 and 6 to make this number sentence correct.

_____ × _____ × _____ + _____ − _____ − _____ = 24

East to west

Learning objectives
(Y4 and Y5) Use all four operations to solve simple word problems involving time.
(Y5) Read the time on a 24-hour digital clock. Use timetables.

Whole class work
Draw the following railway timetable on the board:

Nottingham	09.12	10.36	11.45	12.35	13.55
Chesterfield	09.52	11.13	11.20	13.17	?

● Check that the children can read a 24-hour clock and interpret this timetable, in preparation for the individual activity. Ask questions such as:

What time does the first train arrive at Chesterfield?
How long does the first train take to travel between Nottingham and Chesterfield?
If I miss the 10.36 from Nottingham, how long do I have to wait for the next train?
Which entry in the table is incorrect? Why?
The 12.35 train arrives at Chesterfield at 13.17. What is this time on the 12-hour clock?
When does the last train reach Chesterfield?
Which of the journey times shown is the shortest?

Mental starter
See the starter 35 on page 22.

You will need
Photocopiable page 97 for each child.

Individual/paired work
● Give each child a copy of photocopiable page 97. Go through the timetable with the children. Many adults have difficulty with timetables, and one reason is that they try to take in too much information too quickly. Advise the children to make jottings of the information they have and when they have a difficulty to stop and imagine the actual journey.
● The questions increase in difficulty and later ones require the children to solve multi-step problems. This may require additional support or it may be beneficial for the children to work in pairs.

Plenary
● Refer the children back to the activity sheet and write on the board:
The later trains are all going to travel on to Sheffield. Estimate the time each train will arrive at Chesterfield and Sheffield.
● Discuss with the children that the times between stations vary from train to train by a few minutes and so our answers will only be estimates. If the children are confident, invite them to estimate the earliest and latest times for these trains.

Moving on
● Invite the children to extend the timetable so that the early trains all start from Norwich (or Ely if time is short). Tell them to estimate the times using several of the other trains as examples.

Potential difficulties	Further support
Children may struggle with the use of the 24-hour clock.	Provide children with an analogue clock for reference. If they are still struggling then provide a conversion table from analogue (12-hour) to digital (24-hour).
Children may have difficulty calculating the number of minutes between two times because time is in 'base 60'.	

Name _____

East to west

■ Here is part of a timetable for trains between Norwich and Liverpool. Study it carefully and then try to answer the questions below.

Norwich							12.52	13.49		15.53	16.57	18.45	19.30	20.51
Thetford							13.19	14.16		16.20	17.24	19.12	19.57	21.18
Ely							13.49	14.47			17.51	19.46	20.22	21.46
Peterborough							14.28	15.25		17.15	18.30	20.25	20.55	22.20
Grantham							14.57	15.58		17.49	19.05	21.00		22.55
Nottingham	09.12	10.36	11.45	12.35	13.33	14.38	15.34	16.44	17.32	18.33	19.45	21.40	22.10	23.35
Chesterfield	09.52	11.13	12.20	13.17	14.17	15.16	16.16	17.20	18.12	19.13	20.15			
Sheffield	10.15	11.37	12.39	13.37	14.37	15.35	16.36	17.42	18.35	19.25	20.35			
Stockport	11.22	12.24	13.25	14.23	17.33	16.23	17.23	18.26	19.23	20.23	21.17			
Manchester Piccadilly	11.37	12.37	13.37	14.37	15.37	16.37	17.37	18.37	19.37	20.32	21.28			
Liverpool Lime Street	12.22	14.25	14.25	15.24	16.25	17.25	18.25	19.25	20.25					

1 What time does the earliest train stop at Sheffield? _____

2 What time does the last train stop at Liverpool Lime Street? _____

3 I want to arrive in Nottingham shortly before 8pm. What train should I get from Norwich? _____

4 Estimate when the 19.30 from Norwich passes through Grantham. _____

5 How many minutes does it take from Nottingham to Sheffield on the 11.45? _____

6 How long is the journey from Norwich to Liverpool Lime Street? _____

7 One of the times for the 13.33 from Nottingham is incorrect. Can you find which one and write down the correct time. _____

8 If the 20.51 from Norwich travelled on from Nottingham to Chesterfield, estimate when it would arrive. _____

9 It is proposed that the 14.38 from Nottingham will start earlier from Grantham but still arrive at same time. When should it leave Grantham? _____

50 MATHS LESSONS • AGES 9-11

Reflections

Learning objectives
(Y4) Sketch the reflection of a simple shape in a mirror line.
(Y5) Recognise reflective symmetry in regular polygons.
(Y5) Complete symmetrical patterns with two lines of symmetry at right angles.

Mental starter
See the starter 36 on page 22.

You will need
Photocopiable page 99; mirrors and counters for each child.

Moving on
● Ask the children to return to the activity sheet and to add two more counters to the first drawing, in different colours. Tell them to show the results on the diagrams by adding their two counters in the correct places.
● Give each of the children a small piece of Blu-Tack. Ask them to choose one of the diagrams at the bottom of the page. Invite one of the children to place their piece of Blu-Tack on one of the empty squares. Their partner must reflect this piece in both mirrors and place their piece on a square in the quadrant diagonally opposite. The correct position is equivalent to a half-turn rotation, and the children may come to realise this 'short-cut'.

Whole class work
● Draw the capital letters *A, B, C, D, E* and *F* on the board. Place a tick under those that have a line of symmetry and a cross under those that do not. (Be careful about the letter B, as it depends on how it is drawn.)
● Continue with *G, H* and *I* and ask: *What is the same about the letters with ticks?* Discuss the answers given by the children, including alternative answers. Ask: *What is special about H and I?* (two lines of symmetry).
● Continue through the alphabet, asking the children to identify lines of symmetry. Stop to discuss problematic letters such as Q and U. Some children may want to claim that Y is symmetrical, depending on the way it is written.

Individual work
● Give each child a copy of photocopiable page 99 and a mirror. Ask the children if they can read the title of the activity without the mirror. Check by using the mirror.
● Go through the activity by placing the mirror off-centre (not on one of the mirror lines). Invite the children to view the image in the mirror and make sure they understand the concept of reflecting a point in a line. This activity works well in pairs with one person holding the mirror and the other locating and placing the counters.
● If children find this demanding, consider some additional consolidation work - for example, ask the children to reflect the digits from zero to nine. Discuss the problematic digits in particular, such as one and three.

Plenary
● Ask the children to find words with a vertical line of symmetry about the centre. Good examples include TOT, WOW and TOOT.
● Finally ask them to find words with horizontal symmetry. Assuming the B is allowed then examples include BED, CODE, HOOD and COOKBOOK.

Potential difficulties	Further support
Some children will still have difficulty with reflections and may 'translate' the counters instead.	Have available some reflection pictures. For example, a face that is not symmetrical can be made so with the mirror.

Reflections

■ Add two counters to the diagram below to give it a vertical line of symmetry. Check with a mirror.

■ Draw your solution in the diagram on the right.

■ Now place the two counters in different positions to make the other lines of symmetry.

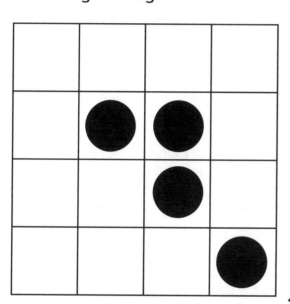
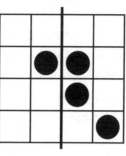
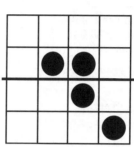
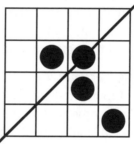
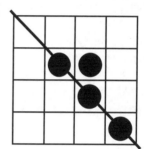

■ Use a mirror to complete these diagrams, to give each of them two lines of symmetry.

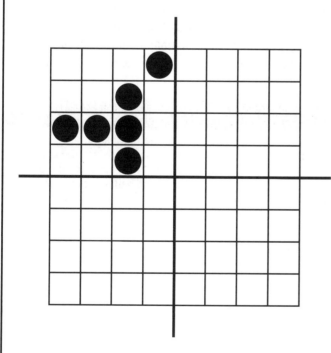
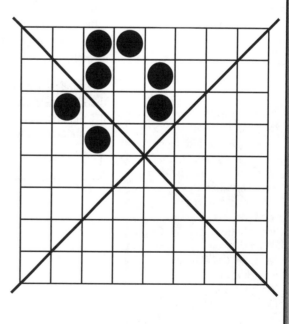

Co-ordinates

Learning objectives
(Y4) Describe and find the position of a point on a grid of squares where the lines are numbered.
(Y5) Read and plot co-ordinates in the first quadrant.
(Y6) Read and plot co-ordinates in all four quadrants.

Mental starter
See the starter 37 on page 23.

You will need
Photocopiable page 101 and squared paper for each child.

Whole class work

● Draw axes on the board, from (0,0) to (6,6). Label the x-axis and the y-axis. You are going to construct a large capital letter M with the children using co-ordinates A(1,2); B(1,6); C(3,4); D(5,6) and E(5,2).
● Mark the first two points, A and B. Ask: *Where is a good place for the centre of the M?* Discuss suggestions and then mark point C. Complete the 'M' together.
● Now write the co-ordinates (2,2) (3,0) (4,1) and (5,0) on the board. Tell the children that these are four of the five co-ordinates of another letter. Ask them to work out what the letter is and to tell you the co-ordinates of the missing point.

Individual work

● Give each child a copy of photocopiable page 101. Make sure that all of the children are happy with the convention that the pair of numbers (3,2) represents the point 3 'across' and 2 'up'. The first part of the activity reinforces this convention by telling children the co-ordinates of a point and by filling in one co-ordinate of the first question for them. Draw their attention to this support.

Plenary

● Draw two more grids on the board, each from (0,0) to (6,6). Draw three corners of a tilted square at points (3,1) (1,3) (5,3). Leave the fourth point (3,5) blank. Tell the children that these are three corners of a square. Ask them to find the fourth point. Add this on the board and make sure that everyone understands that it is a square. Encourage the use of correct language and avoid terms such as 'diamond'.
● On the other diagram draw three corners of the tilted square at points (2,1) (1,4) (4,5). Leave the fourth point (5,2) blank. Tell the children that this is another tilted square. Let them look at the diagram and discuss the options. Some children find it hard to visualise squares in non-standard orientations. When they offer possible co-ordinates ask them for their reasoning.

Moving on
● Set the following challenges. Each of these involves returning to the diagrams on the activity sheet and identifying additional properties.
● In the first diagram, identify the shape ABFC. (Parallelogram)
● In the first diagram, identify the shape BHGF. (Trapezium)
● In the second diagram, find the fourth corner of the square that has CBF for three of its corners.

Potential difficulties	Further support
Children may not be ready for working in all four quadrants.	Cover just the first half of the activity. Return to the activity later, using the first half for consolidation and the second half as 'new work'.

Co-ordinates

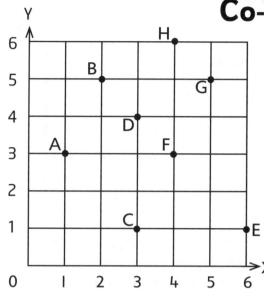

🔲 On these axes check that E is the point (6, 1).

Write down the co-ordinates of B. $(2, \_\_\_)$

Write down the co-ordinates of C. $(\_\_\_, \_\_\_)$

Which letter is at (4, 3)? $\_\_\_$

🔲 Here are four co-ordinates. Write the letters underneath to form a word.

(4, 3)   (1, 3)   (3, 1)   (6, 1)

_____ _____ _____ _____

🔲 Join the letters of this word together with lines. What shape have you made? Write its name here. _____

🔲 Think of a word which can be made from the letters on the grid. Write down the co-ordinates and give it to a partner to solve.

(,   )(,   )(,

🔲 A new point, P, is to be added to the grid so that H, D and P are in a line. Put the point P on the grid.

🔲 Write down the co-ordinates of the point halfway between E and G. (,   )

🔲 In the diagram bottom right, A, B and C are corners of square (A, B, C, D). Mark in point D and draw the square.

The co-ordinates of D are (,   ).

🔲 The co-ordinates E, F and G are three corners of a parallelogram. Find and label the fourth corner H.

🔲 The co-ordinates of H are (,   ).

🔲 Add a new point P to the diagram, half way between J and C. Write the co-ordinates of P on the diagram.

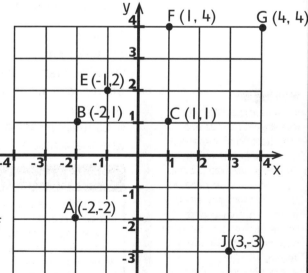

Pyramid puzzle

Figure 1

Learning objectives
(Y4, Y5 and Y6) Solve mathematical problems or puzzles, recognise and explain patterns and relationships.
(Y4, Y5 and Y6) Explain methods and reasoning about numbers orally and in writing.
(Y4, Y5 and Y6) Check with the inverse operation.

Mental starter
See the starter 38 on page 23.

You will need
Photocopiable page 103 for each child; squared paper (or hexagon paper if available).

Whole class work
● Draw the grid (Figure 1) on the board. Explain that the numbers across add up to the missing numbers on the right and that the numbers down add up to the missing numbers at the bottom. Ask the children to complete this grid.

Figure 2

		12
		8
14	6	20

9	4	
8	13	
		34

● Now draw the second grid (Figure 2) and explain that all of the missing numbers are even. Ask: *What could the missing numbers be?* There are several solutions. Ask the children to copy the grid and to see if they can find all of them.

● Finally, ask the children to complete the grid but using four different odd numbers. There is only one solution and it can be arrived at by reasoning or by trial and improvement.

Individual work
● Give each child a copy of photocopiable page 103. Explain that each number is the sum of the two numbers below it. The first example allows the children to become familiar with the idea. The remaining puzzles demand an element of reasoning.
● To support the children, remind them that when solving the number grid puzzles above, they had to experiment to find numbers that fitted the rules. Tell the children to write the numbers in pencil until they are sure and to check their solutions by working from the bottom to the top.

Plenary
● Ask the children to arrange the numbers 1, 2, 3 and 4 in the bottom row of a pyramid, choosing any order. Ask: *What totals are possible in the top row? What is the highest total? How do we have to arrange the numbers?*
● Continue by asking for the lowest totals and finally repeat the activity with the numbers 1, 3, 5, and 7.

Moving on
● Invite the children to investigate the odd and even pattern of numbers arising from this activity. Challenge them to use two odd and two even numbers on the bottom row, arranged in any way they choose. Invite them to find out what happens to the number at the top.
● Ask them to record their findings and to try to explain the result.

Potential difficulties	Further support
Some children may have difficulty recognising and using the operations - some may struggle with questions such as 4 + ___ = 12 and want to write 16 as the answer.	Practise simple examples of number sentences with missing numbers. Explain that if we know 15 + 5 = 17 then we also know 17 - 5 = 12 and 17 - 12 = 5.

Name ______________________

Pyramid puzzle

■ In number pyramids each number is the sum of the two numbers below it. Work out the missing numbers.

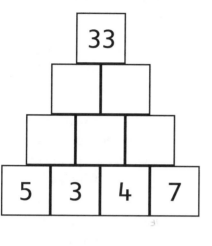

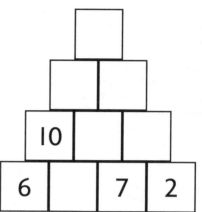

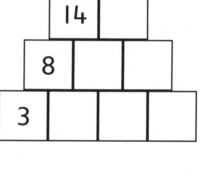

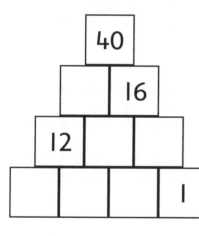

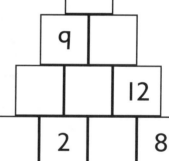

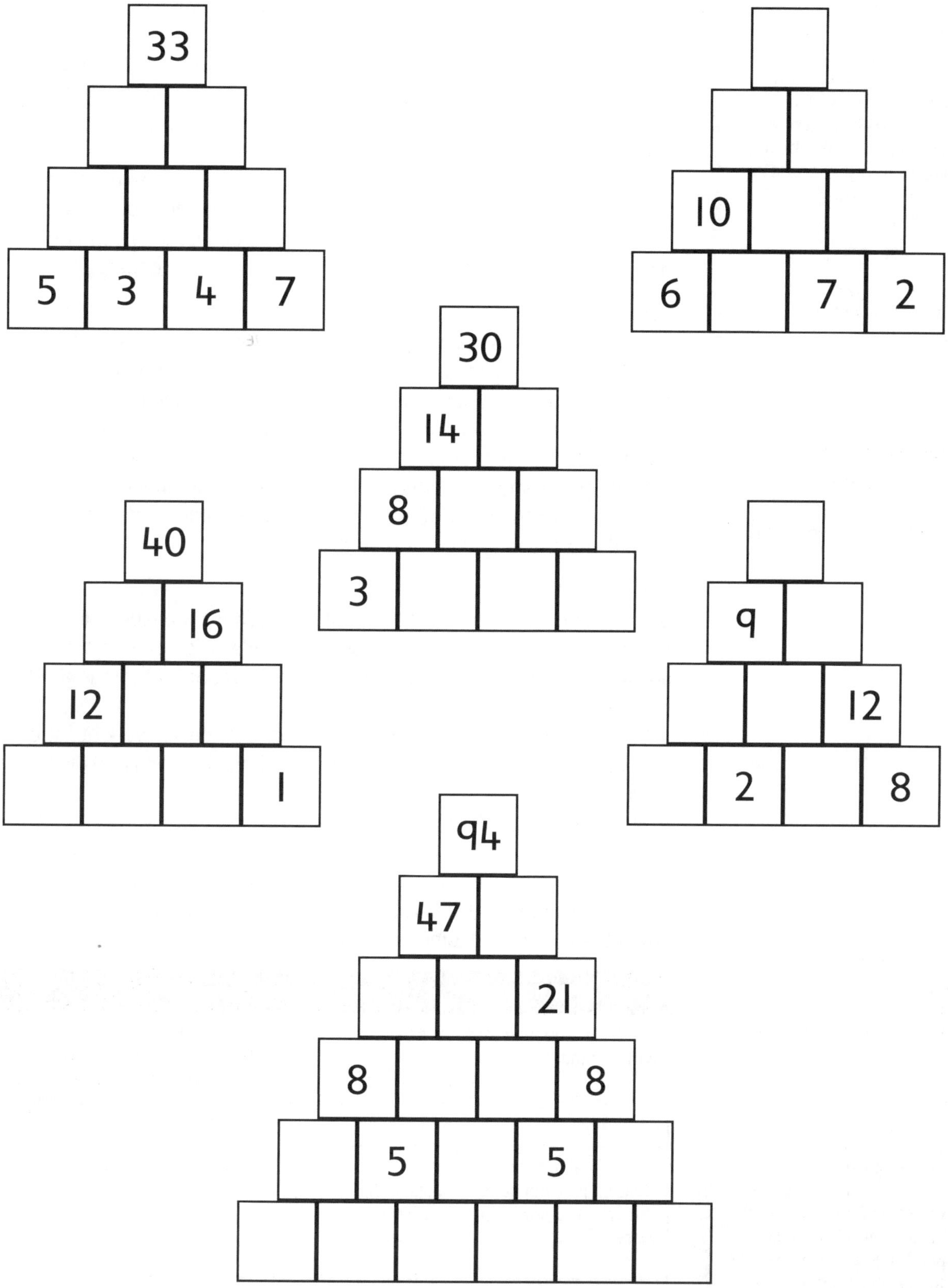

33
5 3 4 7
10
6 7 2
30
14
8
3
40
16
12
1
9
12
2 8
94
47
21
8 8
5 5

Area

Learning objectives
(Y4) Measure and calculate the area of rectangles and other simple shapes, using counting methods and standard units.
(Y5) Understand area measured in square centimetres; understand and use the formula in words 'length × breadth' for the area of a rectangle.

Mental starter
See the starter 39 on page 23.

You will need
Photocopiable page 105 for each child; squared paper.

Whole class work

● Draw a rectangle without dimensions on the board and ask the children for its area. Establish that without the dimensions we cannot find the area. Write dimensions such as 6cm by 5cm along all four edges. Ask the children if they can now find the area.
● Listen carefully to the responses and monitor any misconceptions. Try to avoid emphasising that the 'area is the length × breadth', as this can lead to only a procedural understanding of area, with children having difficulties with compound shapes later.
● Draw a 'wiggly rectangle' on the board. Draw a rectangle inside it and another enclosing it. Say: *Help me to estimate the area of my wiggly shape.* Encourage the children to see that a good estimate will be 'halfway' between the area of the smaller and larger rectangles.

Individual work

● Give each child a copy of photocopiable page 105 and a piece of squared paper for jottings. If the children have difficulty with the concept of area, then allow them to draw each rectangle.
● Encourage the children to find the area by calculation rather than counting. If they are happier counting squares, then work with them on improving this strategy by grouping the smaller squares into 'chunks' that help with the calculation. Try to help the children understand that multiplying the lengths of the edges is a shortcut.

Plenary

● Give each child a piece of squared paper. Draw and label a 6cm by 8cm rectangle on the board and ask the children for its area. When they are satisfied that it is 48cm², ask them to draw another rectangle that has the same area as this one.
● Allow a few minutes for discussion and for them to work out their own methods. Invite the children to offer their solutions and discuss them as a class.
● Now ask the children to find all the rectangles with an area of 48cm².
● Conclude by showing that your original rectangle can be made into many of the others by cutting it up and rearranging it. For example, a 12cm by 4cm rectangle is just a 6cm by 8cm one which has been cut down the middle and joined end to end.

Potential difficulties	Further support
Some children may confuse area with perimeter.	Make sure that the children understand the concept of area as coverage and that multiplying the lengths of the edges of a rectangle is simply a short cut.
In the final part of the activity, children may not cope with bisecting the area and producing two identical pieces.	Allow the children to simply bisect the area.

Moving on
● Ask the children to find the area of their handprint by drawing around their hands on squared paper and then estimating the area.

Name _____

Area

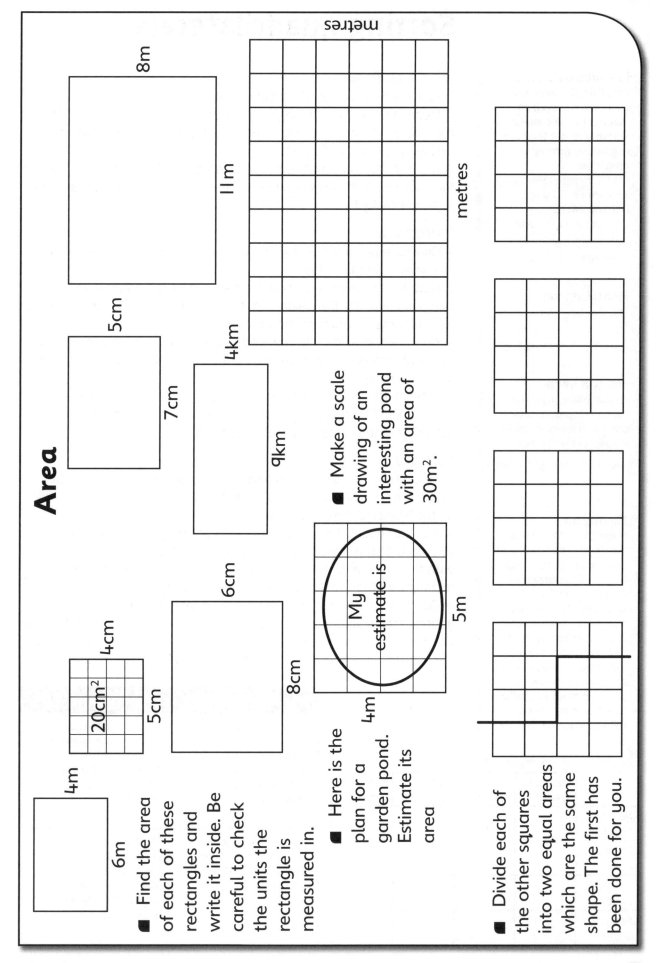

■ Find the area of each of these rectangles and write it inside. Be careful to check the units the rectangle is measured in.

6m
4m

20cm²
4cm
5cm

6cm
8cm
5cm

7cm
5cm

8m
11m

4km
9km

metres

metres

■ Here is the plan for a garden pond. Estimate its area

My estimate is

4m
5m

■ Make a scale drawing of an interesting pond with an area of 30m².

■ Divide each of the other squares into two equal areas which are the same shape. The first has been done for you.

Sorting quadrilaterals

Learning objectives
(Y4) Classify polygons using criteria such as number of right angles, whether or not they are regular, symmetry properties.
(Y5) Recognise reflective symmetry in 2D shapes.
(Y5 and Y6) Identify, estimate and order acute and obtuse angles.

Mental starter
See the starter 40 on page 24.

You will need
Photocopiable page 107, cut into shapes for each child; protractors; enlarged shapes for the teacher.

Moving on
● Ask the children to sort the shapes into an array on an A3 sheet of paper. Along the top of the array mark the number of lines of symmetry. Down the side, mark the number of right angles (see below). Ask the children to paste a copy of the appropriate shape into a cell. Some cells have no shapes in them. One cell has two shapes in it. Ask the children to explain why this is.

Whole class work
● Give each child a set of cut out shapes to use.
● Define the terms 'right angle', 'acute angle', and 'obtuse angle'. Ask the children to hold up a shape with 'four right angles'; 'one right angle'; 'two acute angles' and so on.
● If the children are confident, ask questions such as: *Can you show me the shape with the largest angle?* (The arrowhead – which has a reflex angle internally.)

Paired work
● Give each pair a set of shapes. Ask them to find each shape's name and write it on the shape.
● Now ask the children to examine each shape and draw on any lines of symmetry. Monitor the children at this point as some of them may want to label a line of symmetry on the parallelogram.
● Now ask the children to check the angle of each shape and draw on any right angles (measured using a protractor or the square edge of a piece of paper).
● After all the shapes have been correctly labelled, invite the children to sort them first according to the number of right angles and then according to the number of lines of symmetry.

Plenary
● Make sure that the children have understood a range of properties. Say: *Show me a shape which is a parallelogram.* Most children will hold up the 'standard' parallelogram.
● Ask the children to hold up all of the parallelograms in the set. Discuss the properties of the parallelogram – that it is a quadrilateral with two pairs of parallel sides. (This means that the rhombus, the rectangle and the square are all parallelograms.)
● Conclude by giving a different shape to each child and asking them to arrange themselves in a line. The rule is that as you move along the line the number of properties of a shape increases. The square, at one end, has as many lines of symmetry and as many right angles as possible.

Potential difficulties	Further support
Trouble identifying lines of symmetry on geometric shapes, and may want to draw one on the standard parallelogram.	Fold a shape in half to demonstrate symmetry or have a mirror available to allow the children to see the reflection.
The children may have difficulty if the shape is not in a standard position.	Make sure that the children can identify the properties of a shape and are not simply focusing on the appearance.

	No lines of symmetry	No lines of symmetry	No lines of symmetry	No lines of symmetry
No right angles				
One right angle				
Two right angles				
Four right angles				

Shapes for sorting quadrilaterals

Planning a party

Learning objectives
(Y4) Choose and use appropriate number operations and ways of calculating to solve problems.
(Y4) Solve word problems involving money.
(Y4) Explain methods and reasoning about numbers orally and in writing.
(Y5) Use all four operations to solve simple word problems.
(Y5 and Y6) Develop calculator skills and use a calculator effectively.

Mental starter
See the starter 41 on page 24.

You will need
Photocopiable page 109 for each pair or small group; calculators; paper.

Moving on
● Ask the children to create and price 'healthy option' party food. To do this, they need to add 'healthy' items to the list on the sheet. Prices and package sizes can be found from a shopping list or by using a supermarket website.

Whole class work
● Say: *I want to buy flapjacks for 16 people. They come in packs of six for £1.00. How much do I spend?*
● Write the problem on the board, invite solutions and discuss each idea. Say: *I can buy a larger packet of ten flapjacks for £1.50. Will this reduce the cost?* Discuss solutions and agree the option of buying one packet of each size.
● At each stage ask: *What is the cost per person?* and ensure the correct use of the calculator for checking purposes. Allow the children to discuss the 'fairness' of this calculation, since in the first option there will be two left over. Do we include these in the calculation?

Paired/small group work
● Give out copies of photocopiable page 109. Let the children work in pairs or as a small 'planning group' to support each other.
● Explain that they are planning a party. Show them the lists and the prices. Remind them to be careful as some prices are in pounds and some are in pence.
● Give the children a calculator and some 'jotting' paper. Encourage them to sketch ideas, discuss and plan before completing the list. Let the children make decisions based on what they think people will like and how much food and drink will be consumed. Remind them of the strict budgets.

Plenary
● Use the flapjack prices above to ask the children the best way to buy for parties of different sizes. Display the information in a table such as the one below.

Party size	Pkts of 10	Pkts of 6	Total cost
16	1 £1.50	1 £1.00	£2.50

● Extend the plenary further by asking each child to create a table with additional columns identifying the costs of some of the other items on the party lists (photocopiable page 109).

Potential difficulties	Further support
Difficulties mixing prices marked in pence with those marked in pounds.	Explain the conversion from pounds to pence and revise the notation used.
Use of incorrect notation, such as £2.45p.	
Difficulties handling such a range of information.	Suggest that they start by buying one of each item or pack and then adjust upwards.

Name _____

Planning a party

Party accessories	
Party poppers (pack of 20)	93p
Wacky string (small pack)	98p
Volcanoes (6 pack)	£2.20

Party bag goodies	
Water guns (4 pack)	48p
Pinball games (4 pack)	48p
Maze game (4 pack)	48p
Party blowouts (6 pack)	£1.20
Sliding puzzle (each)	20p

Party food	
Chocolate ice-cream (1 litre tub)	£2.50
Fruit split ice lollies (10 pack)	£1.50
Chocolate brownies (6 pack)	£1.20
Crunchy treat bars (6 pack)	48p
Chocolate birthday cake	£3.60
Jammie Dodgers (250g pack)	90p

Party Drink	
Super fizz cola (2 litres)	£1.30
Orange squash (1 litre)	90p

◢ You are in charge of getting all the material for a birthday party. There will be 20 people.

◢ Make a list here of the accessories. Write down how many you want, the item and the total price.
You are allowed to spend up to £5.00.

__ _____ ____

__ _____ ____

◢ Make a list of items for the party bags. Write down how many you want, the item and the total price. You are allowed to spend up to £10.00.

__ _____ ____

__ _____ ____

◢ Make a list here of the food you will buy. Write down how many you want, the item and the total price.
One chocolate birthday cake is on the list already.
You are allowed to spend up to £12.00.

1 Chocolate birthday cake   £3.60

__ _____ ____

__ _____ ____

__ _____ ____

__ _____ ____

__ _____ ____

__ _____ ____

__ _____ ____

What comes next?

Learning objectives
(Y4) Recognise and extend number sequences formed by counting from any number in steps of constant size.
(Y5) Explain a generalised relationship (formula) in words.
(Y6) Recognise and extend number sequences.

Mental starter
See the starter 42 on page 24.

You will need
Photocopiable page 111 for each child.

Whole class work

● Write the sequence 4, 7, 10, 13, __, __. Ask: *What comes next?*
● Continue with: *How could you describe this sequence?* Encourage the children to specify a sequence in two parts - a starting value and a rule. Both parts are needed to define a sequence.
● Continue with the sequence 5, __, 13, __, 21, 25. The children may want to define the rule in terms of a 'gap' or as counting on. Either way is fine, but establish that the gap is 'hidden' by the choice of terms in the sequence. Encourage the children to use the end of the sequence and work back.
● Repeat with 6, __, 12, __, 18, __ 24. Vary the starting number and the step sizes to avoid a sequence of 'familiar' numbers.

Individual/paired work

● Give each child a copy of photocopiable page 111. Although recording individually the children would benefit from discussion of the rules found. If a child has found a rule, they need to realise that it applies to every term and must not change.
● Offer children support when writing down the rule. It needs to be clear to others and succinct.

Plenary

● Remind the children that sequences can often be extended in both directions.
● Look at the photocopiable activity sheets together. For each sequence ask the children: *What term comes before the first term shown?* This will establish whether the children have an understanding of inverse processes.
● For those sequences in which the children have created their own rules, invite a child to challenge the class, first with *What comes next?* and then with *What comes before?*
● Discuss the problems associated with the picture sequences at the end of the activity. The sequence does not lend itself readily to a term before the one shown. However, the sequence of square numbers offers no such difficulty. Also, the dots are patterns of triangles. Pose the children the question: *Can one dot form a triangle?*

Moving on
● Ask the children to use the activity sheet and to find the tenth value in each sequence. Before they begin, make sure that they are secure in their understanding of each sequence in the activity. Let the children describe a sequence if the tenth value is too difficult to draw or write down.

Potential difficulties	Further support
Some children may want to alter a rule for each term.	If children misunderstand the concept of a sequence then return to very familiar ones and 'make errors'. Write sequences such as 2, 4, 6, 9, 10, 12, and invite the children to say what is wrong with the sequence.

What comes next?

◼ In each sequence, work out the missing numbers.

1) 13, 15, 17, 19, ____, ____, ____   2) 0, 4, 8, 12, ____, ____, ____

3) 40, 37, 34, 31, ____, ____, ____   4) 3, 7, 11, ____, ____, 23, ____

5) 3, ____, 9, ____, 15, ____, 21   6) ____, ____, ____, 29, 36, 43, 50, ____

◼ Decide a rule for yourself.
Write a few terms using your rule.   Write your rule here.

7) 3, ____, ____, ____, ____, ____   _____

_____

8) ____, ____, 12, ____, ____, ____   _____

_____

9) ____, ____, ____, ____, ____, 30   _____

_____

◼ Here are some unusual rules.

10) A, C, E, G, ____, ____, M   11) 0.7, 0.8, 0.9, ____, ____ 1.2

12) M, T, W, ____, F, S, ____   13) 1, 1, 2, 3, 5, 8, ____, ____, 34

◼ Draw the next two diagrams and put in the numbers in these sequences.

14)

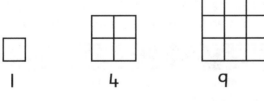

    1   4   9

15)

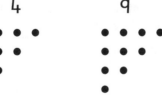

    3   6   10

An unfair spinner

Learning objectives
(Y4) Solve a problem by collecting quickly data in tally charts.
(Y5) Solve a problem by representing and interpreting data in tables, charts, graphs and diagrams.
(Y6) Solve a problem by (representing) **and interpreting information represented in tables, graphs and charts.**

Mental starter
See the starter 43 on page 25.

You will need
Photocopiable page 113 for each child; dice; a bag; three red, two blue and one yellow ball; paper clips.

Whole class work

● Create a tally chart on the board with scores ranging from 2 to 12 to accommodate the scores of two dice.
● Ask the children in pairs to throw two dice, add the scores and record the results on the tally chart.
● Ask each pair to throw the dice five times and jot down the results.
● As you create the tally chart, remind the children about the convention of making the fifth tally a diagonal when collecting in groups of five.
● At the end of the process ask: *Is this a fair way to get numbers between two and 12?* Discuss why this method is unfair – for example, there is only one way to get 12 (double 6), but lots of ways to get seven.

Paired work

● Give each child in the pair a copy of photocopiable page 113 and a paper clip. To use the spinner, place the paper clip in the centre of it and place your pencil at the centre of the spinner. Hold the pencil upright and now flick the paper clip.
● Discuss whether the children think the spinner will give fair or unfair results.
● Ask the children to spin the paper-clip about 100 times and record results on the tally chart. Suggest that they change roles halfway through.

Plenary

● Provide a bag with three red, two blue and one yellow ball in it. Draw an outline tally chart on the board for the three colours and say: *We are going to take a ball out of the bag and record its colour in a tally chart.* Explain that they are going to repeat this action and build up a picture until the tally chart allows them to make an estimate of the colours of the balls in the bag.
● Stop after five goes and invite the children to write down predictions based on the evidence. Stop after another five goes to refine predictions, and stop completely after 24 goes.
● Ask the children to look at the evidence and to estimate the quantity of each ball. Tell them that there are six balls altogether. Take the balls out and allow the children to see the accuracy of their predictions.

Moving on
● Ask the children to gather data from several children to make one large bar graph. Provide squared paper and discuss the scales before they begin.

Potential difficulties	Further support
Some children may be unfamiliar with the conventions of tally charts.	Draw a tally chart to demonstrate.
Some children might have difficulties with the scales on the bar chart.	Monitor children as they draw their first bar. If they are struggling, note their results and place a mark on the axis for them to use.

An unfair spinner

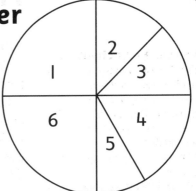

■ Look at the spinner.

Which numbers will be the easiest to get? _____

Explain why. _____

_____

Which number will be the hardest to get? _____

Explain why. _____

Roughly how many more sixes do you expect than fives?

_____

■ Spin the paper clip about 100 times. Create a tally chart by grouping spins of the same type in groups of five. Count the fives and the sixes and then complete this sentence.

I spun roughly _____ sixes for every five.

create a tally chart here

Number	Tally
1	
2	
3	
4	
5	
6	

■ If you had to spin an even number to win a game, would this be a fair spinner? Explain your reasoning here.

_____

_____

_____

_____

_____

_____

Create a bar graph here

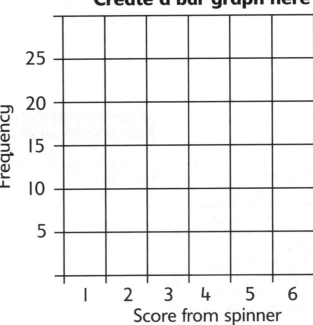

Make 15

Learning objectives
(Y4, Y5 and Y6) Solve mathematical problems or puzzles, recognise and explain patterns and relationships, generalise and predict.
(Y4) Recognise odd and even numbers.
(Y5 and Y6) Make general statements about odd or even numbers.

Mental starter
See the starter 44 on page 25.

You will need
Photocopiable page 115 for each pair; sets of 0 - 9 number cards.

Moving on
● Alter the rules, for example, by including zero – the zero acts as a 'wild card' since it can be placed anywhere.
● Change the central total to 12 and remove the 9. Do not give the children any advice on the central number.

Whole class work
● Give each child a set of 0 - 9 number cards and ask them to put the zero to one side. Say: *Hold up three cards that make 12.* Look at the solutions and make a list of ways of doing this. Leave the list on the board.
● Repeat by asking for three cards that make 15. Again, make a list of possible solutions. Continue by asking for three cards that total 18, then 21 and finally 24. When you get to 24 draw the children's attention to the fact that there is only one solution.
● Finally, ask the children to comment on the way that even and odd numbers have been used to make the various totals. When the total is even, such as 18, the children could choose two odd numbers and one even number (5 + 6 + 7) or three even numbers (4 + 6 + 8). But when the total is odd, they must choose two even numbers and one odd number (3 + 4 + 8) or three odd numbers (1 + 5 + 9).

Paired work
● Give each pair a copy of photocopiable page 115 and one set of number cards. Explain the rules to the children and make sure that they understand them. The game only uses the cards 1 - 9 (no zero) and 5 is always in the middle.
● Clarify some of the rules. For example, if a player makes two lines of 15 when placing a single card, they get two tally marks. (It is possible to make three lines in one go, but only if your opponent is not watching carefully.)
● Encourage the children to develop simple strategies, such as trying to plan a move or two ahead.

Plenary
● Invite the children to offer their strategies for winning.
● Set up a challenge in which the children take on each other in a class competition, with teams. Each team is allowed one minute to discuss their next move.
● Additionally, make this game available to the children when they arrive in the morning so that they begin the day by 'exercising' their brain.

Potential difficulties	Further support
Children are unable to think strategically by looking ahead and planning moves.	Suggest that they look for pairs of numbers that make 10, and set these either side of the 5.

Make 15

◼ Rules of the game

Fill in the names of the two players in the score card.

You need one set of 0 – 9 number cards.

Remove the zero and place the 5 in the centre of the grid.

Shuffle and deal the rest of the cards, four to each player.

Players take turns to place a card. The aim is to make any row, column or diagonal add to 15. Once placed, a card cannot be moved.

When you make 15, place a tally mark on your score card.

When all cards have been placed, start again.

After three games, add up the tally points to find a winner.

Score cards

Name	15s made	Total

Name	15s made	Total

PHOTOCOPIABLE

www.scholastic.co.uk   **50 MATHS LESSONS · AGES 9-11**

Triangle number puzzles

Learning objectives
(Y4, Y5 and Y6) Solve mathematical problems or puzzles, recognise and explain patterns and relationships, generalise and predict.

Mental starter
See the starter 45 on page 26.

You will need
Photocopiable page 117 for each child; a set of 0 - 9 number cards; small pre-cut circles of paper.

Whole class work

Draw the boxes (shown right) on the board. Tell the children that the numbers in the squares add up to each of the numbers in the circles between them.

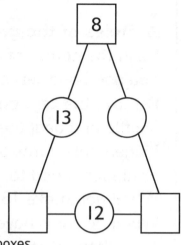

● Ask: *Which box should I work out first?* Help the children to develop strategies for working through these puzzles in a logical order, using reasoning before trial and improvement. Once the box in the bottom left corner is filled, it should be natural for the children to progress anti-clockwise to complete the other two boxes.

Individual work

● Give each child a copy of photocopiable page 117 and a set of 0 - 9 number cards. Explain that each puzzle can be solved by using cards from just one set. Suggest that they put the number cards on their desk to look like the arrangement in the puzzle.
● Draw the children's attention to the arrows in Puzzle 1 (indicating that the numbers in each box add in the direction of the arrows). In addition, go through the idea for Puzzles 3 and 4, in which the numbers in the squares add to give the numbers in the circles. Provide some pre-cut circles of paper for the children to use to try out combinations.

Plenary

● Focus upon the children's reasoning skills as they go through their solutions. For each puzzle ask: *What was the first number you found? Why was this the first number?*

Moving on
● Ask the children to look at the second puzzle again and to investigate which numbers are possible along the sides of a triangle. If necessary, suggest that they use the same numbers from the original solution, 1, 2, 3, 4, 5 and 6, but arrange them differently.
● Let the children create their own puzzles in a similar way to Puzzle 4. Suggest to the children that they create the solution first and then rub out three numbers.

Potential difficulties	Further support
Puzzle 1 - using an unstructured approach.	Suggest that the children try different numbers in the top box and then look for pairs of numbers to fit below it.
Puzzle 2 - unable to find the solutions.	Suggest that the children work with the smaller numbers because the total required is low.
Puzzle 3 - unable to understand the nature of the problem.	The use of circles is to make the puzzle easier to understand. Some of the numbers given are two-digit numbers, but those missing require only a single digit.
Puzzle 4 - unable to find a suitable strategy.	Suggest that the children make pairs of numbers that add to the numbers in the circle and use those that have numbers in common. If necessary, provide the clue that all of the numbers they need to use are odd (5, 7 and 9 are needed).

Triangle number puzzles

Puzzle 1

▟ Make each box add up to the two just below it.

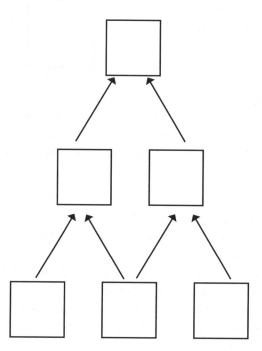

Puzzle 2

▟ Make all three sides of the triangle add up to 9.

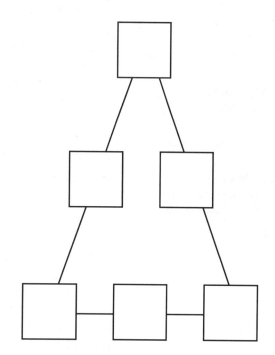

Puzzle 3

▟ Make the numbers either side of a circle add to the number in the circle.

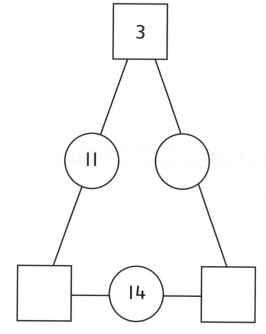

Puzzle 4

▟ Make the numbers either side of a circle add to the number in the circle.

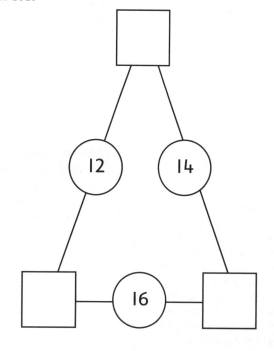

Square number puzzles

Whole class work
● Draw the puzzle shown (Figure 1) on the board.
● Emphasise the grid lines in the puzzle. Tell the children that there must be a 1, 2, 3 and 4 in each row, in each column, and in each grid of four squares.
● Invite the children to discuss where they think the first missing number should go. (It has to be the 3 in the top row.)
● Ask: *What number can we work out next?* Most children will only need a moment or two to spot the missing 4 on the bottom row.
● Continue in this way, allowing discussion time when the reasoning becomes more complicated.

1	2		4
		2	
	3	1	
			3

Figure 1

Individual work
● Give each child a copy of photocopiable page 119. Tell the children that each puzzle can be solved, without guessing, by identifying the numbers that must go in a box.
● Suggest that the children complete the puzzles in pencil first. Explain that the puzzles get progressively more difficult.
● Consider making the puzzles more of a visual or kinaesthetic exercise by enlarging them on a photocopier and giving the children small number cards to move around.

Plenary
● Go through the solutions with the children, focusing upon their methods of reasoning. For example, for each puzzle ask: *What was the first number you found? Why was this the first number?*
● Draw the puzzle shown (Figure 2) on the board. Explain that it is a difficult puzzle. Suggest that they discuss with other children where they think the first number should go. Invite the children to rehearse their reasoning with each other, so that they can explain to the rest of the class why they have chosen a particular number.

3			
	1	3	
	2		
4			1

Figure 2

Learning objectives
(Y4, Y5 and Y6) Solve mathematical problems or puzzles, recognise and explain patterns and relationships, generalise and predict.

Mental starter
See the starter 46 on page 26.

You will need
Photocopiable page 119 for each child; squared paper.

Moving on
● Provide squared paper for the children to use and invite them to make their own puzzles in this format. Suggest that to create one, they start with a solution and then repeatedly remove numbers. Check each time that the puzzle is possible.

Potential difficulties	Further support
Difficulties in identifying suitable strategies for the puzzles (in particular knowing that what a number is *not* can be important in solving a puzzle).	Point to a square and say: *What number(s) could this be? What number(s) can it not be?* Ensure that you explain why to the children.

Square number puzzles

■ The numbers 1, 2, 3 and 4 must appear just once in each row, each column and in each group of four squares. The grid on the right has been filled in as an example.

1	2	3	4
3	4	2	1
4	3	1	2
2	1	4	3

4		3	2
2	3	4	1
	2		
1		2	

2	1	3	
3		1	2
	2		
		2	1

2	1		3
	4		1
1			
		1	

4	1		
3		1	
	3		
2			

Pentominoes

Whole class work

● Show the children one pentomino and ask: *How many squares are joined to make this shape?* (five squares). Draw the shape on the board.
● Challenge the children to arrange five squares in a different way. Invite any new ways of arranging the pieces to be added to the board, to build up a collection.
● Now ask the children to find all the different ways of arranging five squares (there are 12 different arrangements).
● As the children offer new 'solutions', ask them to check carefully for duplicates. Make sure that they understand what 'different' means in this context.

Individual work

● Give each child a set of 'Pentominoes'. Each of the pentominoes is traditionally named after the letter of the alphabet it resembles (see right, which also shows a solution to forming a 10 × 6 rectangle and two solutions for 6 × 5 rectangles).
● Invite the children to take three of the pentominoes to make a rectangle. Once each child is successful, ask them: *What is the same about all of the rectangles?* (There are many solutions but all of them produce a 5 × 3 rectangle.)
● Ask the children if they could have predicted what size rectangle

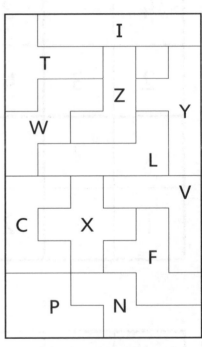

three pieces would produce. If necessary, explain that three pieces have 15 squares and that 5 × 3 is the only rectangle possible. Invite the children to record some 5 × 3 rectangles.
● Now ask what size of rectangle the children could make with four pieces, five pieces and so on. It is possible to make all rectangles that are multiples of 5, between 15 and 60, many of them in different sizes such as 20 × 3 and 10 × 6. Most of these larger ones are very hard to find.
● Once the children have recorded a few successful rectangles, allow them time to set their own challenges.

Plenary

● Invite the children to share their solutions and surprises. Some of them may have challenges to set for the other children.

Potential difficulties	Further support
Most children can tackle this activity with confidence since it is open and unthreatening. However, some children may become frustrated if they are not successful.	Make sure that *any* rectangle the children produce (or other interesting shape) is recorded as a successful outcome.

Pentominoes

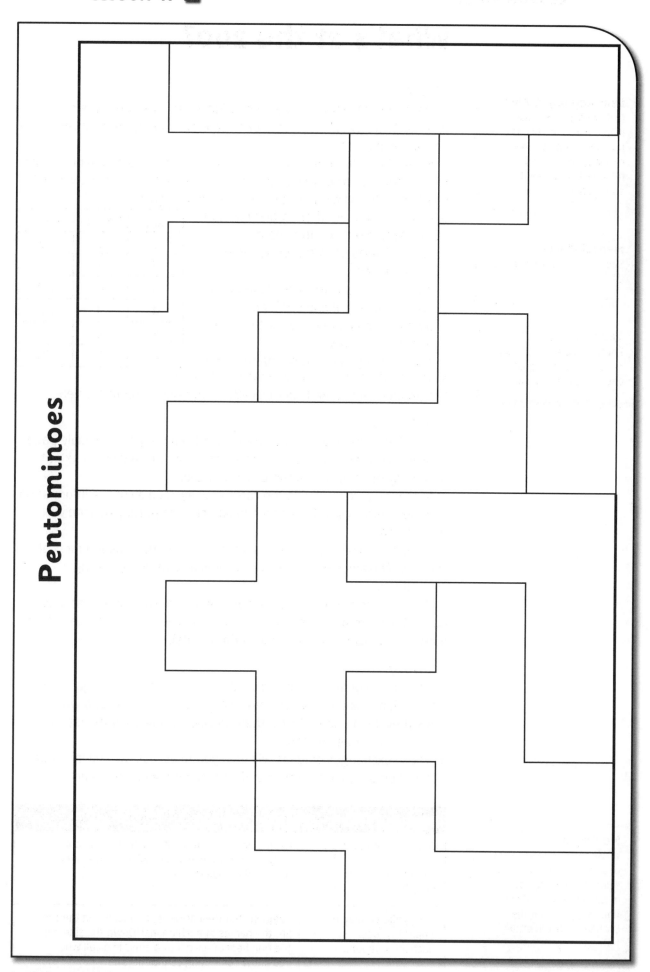

What's at the zoo?

Learning objectives
(Y4, Y5 and Y6) Solve mathematical problems or puzzles, recognise and explain patterns and relationships, generalise and predict.

Mental starter
See the starter 48 on page 27.

You will need:
Photocopiable page 123 for each pair (cards copied and cut out); squared paper.

Whole class work

● On the board, write: *I have 7 pets. Some are cats and some are parrots. There are 24 legs between them. How many cats are there and how many parrots?*

● Invite the children to think about this problem for a few minutes and then to suggest how they could solve it. One method is to draw a table, which includes all the possibilities (see below right).

● Continue with another problem written as four statements on the board:

> *I have 3 sorts of fruit (apples, oranges and bananas).*
> *There are 13 pieces of fruit altogether.*
> *I have twice as many apples as oranges, and more bananas than both of these together.*
> *I have at least two pieces of each fruit.*

Cats	Parrots	Legs
1	6	16
2	5	18
3	4	20
4	3	22
5	2	24
6	1	26

● The children may need guidance in starting this problem. A trial and improvement strategy is appropriate here.

Paired work

● Give the children a pre-cut set of cards from the photocopiable page. Explain that they must use the information on the cards to work out how many of each animal there is at the zoo.

● Invite the pairs to divide the cards equally, read all of the information and then discuss which cards are most useful in getting started with the problem.

● Advise the children to jot down partial solutions or useful facts along the way. The aim here is to work towards a solution by testing possibilities.

● Allow the children to test their answers by making sure that they match the statements on every card (the answers are: two tigers, three lions, four snakes, six ducks and eight parrots).

Plenary

● Ask the children what they talked about and how they organised the information. Ask them which cards were the most useful and which cards they left for later. Invite them to discuss any breakthrough or discovery that helped them.

● These exchanges of ideas will help you to assess the children, but will also enrich their experience of dealing with word problems.

Moving on
● Ask the children to think of a problem with only one solution, which can be reached in a fairly short time. Suggest that they continue to use the 'zoo' format.

Potential difficulties	Further support
Unable to interpret the word problem or find suitable strategies to solve it.	Offer clues in the form of advice. For example, suggest that they work out whether the number of animals is odd or even.
Some children may find it hard to process so much information.	Suggest that they draw up a table. Along the top are the names of each animal. Down the side are the numbers of each. Put a cross in a cell when you know something cannot be true.

What's at the zoo?

The zoo only has lions, tigers, ducks, parrots and snakes.	The animals have 48 legs altogether.
There is a different number of each animal.	There are two more ducks than snakes.
There are twice as many ducks as lions.	There are more parrots than any other animal.
There are 23 animals in the zoo.	The lions and tigers have 20 legs between them.
There are twice as many snakes as tigers.	The birds have 28 legs between them.

Tangrams

Whole class work

● Draw an accurate square on the board and divide each edge into two with small marks. Tell the children what you have done. Draw a line to create the large right-angled triangle in the top right, by joining one of these marks to a corner, as shown right. (Do not draw the remainder of the lines shown dotted at this stage.)

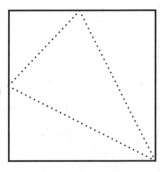

● Say: *I have made a triangle by cutting the corner. How many of these triangles will fit into the square?* Allow the children to draw their own square to experiment.

● Draw another line to create the smaller right-angled triangle shown top left. Ask the children how many of these smaller triangles will fit into the square. The children will need to draw their own copy and to experiment. Do not prompt too quickly with the suggestion that they draw horizontal and vertical lines, to divide the square.

● Finally, draw the third line and ask the children how many of the triangles shown bottom-left will fit into the square. For some this is obviously the same as the first triangle, but flipped over, while others may need a little prompting.

Individual work

● Provide each child with a cut-out set of tangrams. Allow them to explore the shapes with the larger pieces. Challenge them to make squares using one, then two, three, four and finally five pieces. Ask them to record each one on squared paper. Suggest a standard recording size that is the same as that of the smaller whole tangram (8cm by 8cm). Tell them that it is impossible to make a square with six pieces.

● Allow the children 'free time' to explore the pieces. Suggest that they try to use all of the pieces and arrange them to look like different animals.

Plenary

● Share the variety of ways of making squares using from one to five pieces. An overhead projector is useful here to allow you to set up the solutions easily, for all the children to see.

● Finally, invite the children to share any interesting shapes which they have made. These could form the basis of a display.

Potential difficulties	Further support
Some children may struggle to make squares in the individual work.	Show the children that some edges of the tangram match and that they should try these first when looking for a square.

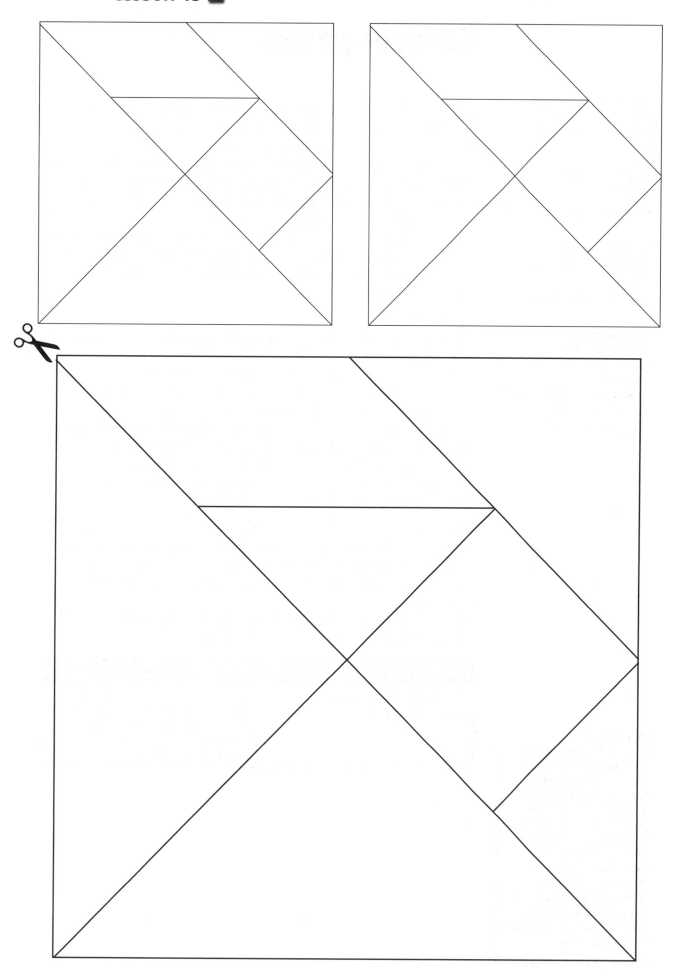

Counter games

Mental starter
See the starter 50 on page 27.

You will need
Photocopiable page 127; four red counters and four blue counters for each pair; two large red and two large blue discs; Blu-Tack.

Whole class work

● Draw a copy of the 'Block them in' game board (see photocopiable page 127) for the class to see. Place two red discs over the top blobs and two blue discs over the bottom blobs.
● Describe the rules of the game to the children. Tell them that a player may slide a counter to the empty blob, but they may not jump over their opponent. Invite two children to play, while the class watches. Ask those watching to see if they can spot a winning strategy.
● After the game, discuss winning strategies with the children. Play the game again with another two children. Suggest to these children that they try some of the strategies offered by the class. Ask the children if they think the game is fair.

Paired work

● Give each pair of children a copy of photocopiable page 127 and some blue and red counters.
● Tell the children to begin with 'Block them in'. Ask: *Is it better to be at the top or the bottom?; Is it better to go first or second?* Suggest that they record the outcome of a number of games to help them decide.
● When the children move on to the other games, explain that they are similar to noughts and crosses, but with these games you are allowed to move your pieces. Remind them that they cannot move diagonally. Invite the children to find any winning strategies and decide if there is an advantage to going first.

Plenary

● Talk about the first noughts and crosses style game with the class. Discuss whether there is an advantage of holding the central square. Ask the children how often they won when they did not have the central square.
● If you wish to play the games as a class, copy the board onto a transparency and use it on an overhead projector.

Potential difficulties	Further support
The children may struggle to articulate a strategy.	Play a game against a child. As you play, invite the child to explain why he or she made the move. Suggest looking ahead to see what their opponent might do next.

Moving on
● Suggest to the children that they return to the second and third games in turn. Ask them to label the rows and columns of the grid with letters along the bottom and numbers up the sides. Ask them to play a game and to record the moves. After the game, analyse the moves, deciding whether one player could have made a better move or if the game is fair.

Counter games

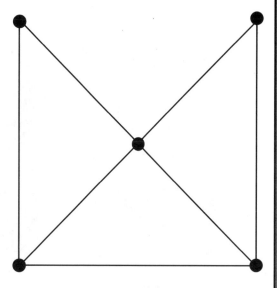

Block them in

- One player needs two red counters and the other needs two blue ones.
- One player covers the top two blobs and the other covers the bottom two.
- One player starts and slides a counter along a black line to an empty blob.
- To win you must block your opponent so they cannot move.

Three in a row

- For each game below, one player needs red counters and the other needs blue ones. To start, one player covers the crosses, the other covers the circles.
- A player moves by sliding a counter horizontally or vertically (not diagonally) into an empty square.
- To win, you must get three of your counters in a row, horizontally, vertically or diagonally.

X	O	X	O
O	X	O	X

X	O	X
O	X	O

- Can you find a winning strategy?
- Does it matter who goes first?